Edexcel
GCSE MODULAR MATHEMATICS
Examples and Practice

HIGHER

Stage 2

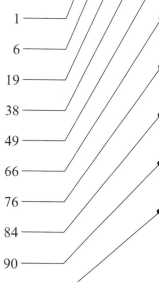

Heinemann

Edexcel
Success through qualifications

About this book

This *Examples and Practice* book is designed to help you get the best possible grade in your Edexcel GCSE maths examination. The authors are senior examiners and coursework moderators and have a good understanding of Edexcel's requirements.

Higher Stage 2 Examples and Practice covers all the topics that will be tested in your Higher Stage 2 examination. You can use this book to revise in the run up to your exam, or you can use it throughout the course, alongside the *Edexcel GCSE Maths* Higher core textbook.

References in the contents list for each section of the book tell you where to find the most relevant paragraph of the specification. For example, NA2a refers to Number and Algebra, paragraph 2, section a.

Helping you prepare for your exam

To help you prepare, each topic offers:
- **Key points** to reinforce the key teaching concepts
- **Teaching references** showing you where the relevant material is covered in both the old and new editions of the *Edexcel GCSE Maths* Higher core textbook. These references show you where to find full explanations of concepts, and additional worked examples e.g.

Teaching reference:
(pp 47–49, section 3.1, 3.2) —————— The first reference is to the old edition
pp 53–56, section 3.2, 3.3 —————— The second reference is to the new edition

Where material is new to the new specification there is no reference to the old edition textbooks.
- **Worked examples** showing you how to tackle a problem and lay out your answer
- **Exercises** with references showing you which exercises in the *Edexcel GCSE Maths* Higher core textbook contain similar questions. The first reference, in brackets and italic, is to the old edition. The second reference is to the new edition
- **A summary of key points** so you can check that you have covered all the key concepts

Exam practice and using the answers

An exam style practice paper at the back of the book will help you make sure that you are totally exam-ready. This paper is exactly the same length and standard as your actual Stage 2 exam.

Answers to all the questions are provided at the back of the book. Once you have completed an exercise you can use the answers to check whether you have made any mistakes. You need to show full working in your exam – it isn't enough to write down the answer.

Which edition am I using?

The new editions of the *Edexcel GCSE Maths* core textbooks have yellow cover flashes saying "ideal for the 2001 specification". You can also use the old edition (no yellow cover flash) to help you prepare for your Stage 1 exam.

Contents

Heinemann Educational Publishers,
Halley Court, Jordan Hill, Oxford, OX2 8EJ
a division of Reed Educational & Professional Publishing Ltd
Heinemann is a registered trademark of Reed Educational & Professional Publishing Ltd

OXFORD MELBOURNE AUCKLAND
JOHANNESBURG BLANTYRE GABORONE
IBADAN PORTSMOUTH NH (USA) CHICAGO

First published 2002

ISBN 0 435 53549 8

06 05 04 03 02
10 9 8 7 6 5 4 3 2 1

Designed and typeset by Tech-Set Ltd, Gateshead, Tyne and Wear
Cover photo: Digitalvision
Cover design by Miller, Craig and Cocking
Printed in the United Kingdom by Scotprint

Acknowledgements
The publishers and authors would like to thank Jean Linsky for her assistance with the manuscript.

The answers are not the responsibility of Edexcel.

Publishing team	Design	Production	Author team
Editorial	Phil Richards	David Lawrence	Karen Hughes
Sue Bennett	Colette Jacquelin	Jason Wyatt	Trevor Johnson
Lauren Bourque			Peter Jolly
Des Brady			David Kent
Nicholas Georgiou			Keith Pledger
Derek Huby			
Maggie Rumble			
Nick Sample			
Harry Smith			
Isabel Thomas			

Tel: 01865 888058 www.heinemann.co.uk

1 Index notation and standard form

1.1 Zero, negative and fractional indices

- $x^0 = 1$ for all non-zero values of x.

- $x^{-n} = \dfrac{1}{x^n}$ (where $x \neq 0$).

- $x^{\frac{1}{n}} = \sqrt[n]{x}$

- $x^{\frac{m}{n}} = (\sqrt[n]{x})^m$ or $x^{\frac{m}{n}} = \sqrt[n]{x^m}$

> The reciprocal of 5 is $\frac{1}{5}$. Multiplying a number by its reciprocal gives 1; for example,
>
> $5 \times \frac{1}{5} = 1$ and $x^2 \times \dfrac{1}{x^2} = 1$.

Example 1

Write down the reciprocal of:

(a) 8   (b) y (c) x^2 (d) $\frac{2}{3}$

(a) $\frac{1}{8}$ (b) $\frac{1}{y}$ (c) $\frac{1}{x^2}$ (d) $\frac{3}{2}$

Example 2

Find the value of:

(a) 3^0 (b) 3^{-2} (c) $16^{\frac{1}{2}}$ (d) $8^{-\frac{1}{3}}$ (e) $8^{\frac{2}{3}}$

(a) $3^0 = 1$

(b) $3^{-2} = \dfrac{1}{3^2} = \dfrac{1}{9}$

(c) $16^{\frac{1}{2}} = \sqrt[2]{16} = 4$

(d) $8^{-\frac{1}{3}} = \dfrac{1}{8^{\frac{1}{3}}} = \dfrac{1}{\sqrt[3]{8}} = \dfrac{1}{2}$

(e) $8^{\frac{2}{3}} = (\sqrt[3]{8})^2 = 2^2 = 4$

Exercise 1A   Links (*1H, 20C, 20D*) 1H, 20C, 20D

1 Write down the reciprocal of:

   (a) 3   **(b)** 4   **(c)** a **(d)** $2a$ **(e)** y^3 **(f)** $\frac{3}{4}$ **(g)** $\frac{2}{5}$

2 Find the value of:

   (a) 4^{-2} **(b)** 8^{-2} **(c)** 3^{-3} **(d)** 2^{-4} **(e)** $36^{\frac{1}{2}}$

   (f) $100^{\frac{1}{2}}$ **(g)** $8^{\frac{1}{3}}$ **(h)** $1000^{\frac{1}{3}}$ **(i)** $25^{-\frac{1}{2}}$ **(j)** $49^{-\frac{1}{2}}$

   (k) $27^{-\frac{1}{3}}$ **(l)** $64^{-\frac{1}{3}}$ **(m)** 8^0 **(n)** 2^0 **(o)** $64^{\frac{2}{3}}$

   (p) $8^{\frac{5}{3}}$ **(q)** $25^{\frac{3}{2}}$ **(r)** $1000^{-\frac{2}{3}}$ **(s)** $27^{-\frac{4}{3}}$ **(t)** $4^{-\frac{5}{2}}$

1.2 Using index laws

- $x^n \times x^m = x^{n+m}$

- $x^n \div x^m = x^{n-m}$ or $\dfrac{x^n}{x^m} = x^{n-m}$

- $(x^n)^m = x^{n \times m}$

Example 3
Simplify the following expressions:

(a) $x^2 \times x^{-3}$ (b) $\dfrac{x^{-4}}{x^2}$ (c) $x^{\frac{1}{2}} \times x^3$ (d) $(x^{\frac{1}{2}})^4$

(a) $x^2 \times x^{-3} = x^{2+(-3)} = x^{-1}$

(b) $\dfrac{x^{-4}}{x^2} = x^{-4-2} = x^{-6}$

(c) $x^{\frac{1}{2}} \times x^3 = x^{\frac{1}{2}+3} = x^{3\frac{1}{2}} = x^{\frac{7}{2}}$

(d) $(x^{\frac{1}{2}})^4 = x^{\frac{1}{2} \times 4} = x^{\frac{4}{2}} = x^2$

Example 4
Simplify and evaluate the following expressions:

(a) $4^{-\frac{1}{2}} \times 4^2$ (b) $\dfrac{3^2 \times 3^{-3}}{3^{-4}}$ (c) $(5^{\frac{1}{2}})^6$

(a) $4^{-\frac{1}{2}} \times 4^2 = 4^{-\frac{1}{2}+2} = 4^{\frac{3}{2}}$

     $4^{\frac{3}{2}} = (\sqrt{4})^3 = 2^3 = 8$

(b) $\dfrac{3^2 \times 3^{-3}}{3^{-4}} = \dfrac{3^{2+(-3)}}{3^{-4}} = \dfrac{3^{-1}}{3^{-4}} = 3^{-1-(-4)} = 3^3$

     $3^3 = 27$

(c) $(5^{\frac{1}{2}})^6 = 5^{\frac{1}{2} \times 6} = 5^3$

     $5^3 = 125$

Exercise 1B   **Links (*1G, 1H*) 1G, 1H**

1   Simplify the following expressions:

     (a) $x^3 \times x^2$ (b) $y^{-2} \times y^4$ (c) $a^{\frac{1}{2}} \times a^{\frac{3}{2}}$

     (d) $\dfrac{t^4}{t^5}$ (e) $(c^2)^3$ (f) $(p^{\frac{1}{2}})^3$

     (g) $\dfrac{z^0 \times z^2}{z^{-3}}$ (h) $r^{-\frac{2}{3}} \times r^{\frac{3}{2}}$ (i) $\dfrac{s^{-3} \times s^2}{s^4}$

     (j) $\dfrac{3x^2 \times 2x^3}{2x^4}$ (k) $\dfrac{2x^{\frac{1}{2}} \times 5x^{-2}}{4x^3}$

2 Simplify and evaluate the following expressions:

(a) $2^3 \times 2^{-4}$ (b) $3^{\frac{1}{2}} \times 3^{\frac{3}{2}}$ (c) $8^{-\frac{1}{3}} \times 8^1$

(d) $(2^4)^{\frac{1}{2}}$ (e) $\dfrac{6^1 \times 6^3}{6^6}$ (f) $\dfrac{4^{\frac{3}{2}} \times 4^{\frac{1}{2}}}{4^2}$

(g) $(8^{\frac{2}{3}})^3$ (h) $\dfrac{(4^{\frac{1}{2}})^5}{4^2}$ (i) $(4^2)^{-\frac{3}{2}}$

(j) $\dfrac{9^0 \times 9^{\frac{1}{2}}}{9^2}$

1.3 Calculations using standard form

Teaching reference:
(*pp 114–115, section 5.9*)
pp 118–121, section 5.10

Example 5

Work out:

(a) $(3.4 \times 10^5) \times (2.6 \times 10^3)$

(b) $\dfrac{(5.8 \times 10^4)}{(8.5 \times 10^6)}$,

Remember: a number in standard form is written in the form $a \times 10^n$ where a is a number between 1 and 10 and n is an integer.

giving your answers in standard form.

(a) $(3.4 \times 10^5) \times (2.6 \times 10^3)$
$= (3.4 \times 2.6) \times (10^5 \times 10^3)$
$= 8.84 \times 10^{(5+3)}$
$= 8.84 \times 10^8$ ———————————— Check answer is in standard form.

(b) $\dfrac{5.8 \times 10^4}{8.5 \times 10^6} = \dfrac{5.8}{8.5} \times \dfrac{10^4}{10^6}$
$= 0.682\,352\,941 \times 10^{(4-6)}$
$= 0.682\,352\,941 \times 10^{-2}$ ———— Answer is not in standard form.
$= 6.82 \times 10^{-3}$ (3 s.f.)

■ **Standard form can be used to make approximations and estimates.**

Example 6

Work out an estimate for:
(a) $537\,890 \times 0.003\,12$
(b) $0.0921 \div 0.000\,331$.

(a) $537\,890 \times 0.003\,12$
$= 5.3789 \times 10^5 \times 3.12 \times 10^{-3}$ Rewrite in standard form.
$\approx 5 \times 10^5 \times 3 \times 10^{-3}$ Write the numbers correct to 1 s.f.
$= (5 \times 3) \times (10^5 \times 10^{-3})$
$= 15 \times 10^2$
$= 1500$

(b) $0.0921 \div 0.000\,331$

$$= \frac{9.21 \times 10^{-2}}{3.31 \times 10^{-4}}$$

$$\approx \frac{9 \times 10^{-2}}{3 \times 10^{-4}}$$

$$= \frac{9}{3} \times \frac{10^{-2}}{10^{-4}}$$

$$= 3 \times 10^2$$

$$= 300$$

Exercise 1C   Links (5Q) 5R

In questions **1–4** do not use a calculator.

1   Evaluate these expressions, giving your answer in standard form:
  (a) $(5 \times 10^4) \times (3 \times 10^3)$ (b) $(2.1 \times 10^{-3}) \times (5 \times 10^2)$
  (c) $(1.8 \times 10^7) \times (2 \times 10^{-4})$ (d) $(4.8 \times 10^{-2}) \times (8 \times 10^7)$
  (e) $(2.7 \times 10^{-2}) \div (9 \times 10^4)$ (f) $(6.4 \times 10^6) \div (1.6 \times 10^3)$
  (g) $\dfrac{5.5 \times 10^3}{1.1 \times 10^2}$ (h) $\dfrac{3.6 \times 10^{-6}}{4 \times 10^3}$

2   Evaluate the following expressions, giving your answers as ordinary decimal numbers:
  (a) $(3 \times 10^4) \times (7 \times 10^3)$ (b) $(2.3 \times 10^{-2}) \times (1.6 \times 10^4)$
  (c) $(3.8 \times 10^{-4}) \times (8 \times 10^{-3})$ (d) $(6.2 \times 10^3) \div (4 \times 10^2)$
  (e) $\dfrac{4.8 \times 10^{-4}}{6 \times 10^3}$ (f) $\dfrac{3.55 \times 10^{-4}}{5 \times 10^{-2}}$

3   Estimate the value of the following:
  (a) $73\,261 \times 39.478$ (b) $896.25 \times 0.003\,21$
  (c) 638.2×5.987 (d) $0.002\,58 \times 0.794$
  (e) $82.63 \div 0.004\,23$ (f) $15.63 \div 0.0278$
  (g) $9300\,000 \div 4187$ (h) $0.000\,28 \div 0.007\,38$

> Hint: rewrite the numbers in standard form to 1 s.f.

4   The distance from the Earth to the Sun is 1.5×10^8 km.
  The distance from Neptune to the Sun is 4.5×10^9 km.
  How many times further from the Sun is Neptune than the Earth?

5   The United Kingdom has an area of 2.5×10^5 km^2 and a population of 5.5×10^7 people.
  Calculate the number of people per km^2 in the UK.

6   The mass of a neutron is 1.675×10^{-24} grams.
  Calculate the total mass of 5×10^6 neutrons. Give your answer in standard form.

Exercise 1D   **Mixed questions**

1 Write down the reciprocal of:
(a) 9   (b) $3x$ (c) $\frac{4}{5}$

2 Find the value of:
(a) 6^{-2} (b) 8^0 (c) 2^{-3} (d) $49^{\frac{1}{2}}$
(e) $8^{\frac{1}{3}}$ (f) $27^{\frac{2}{3}}$ (g) $81^{-\frac{1}{2}}$ (h) $25^{-\frac{3}{2}}$

3 Simplify the following expressions:
(a) $y^3 \times y^{-4}$ (b) $\frac{y^6}{y^{-2}}$ (c) $y^{\frac{3}{2}} \times y^4$
(d) $(y^{\frac{1}{3}})^{-4}$ (e) $4y^2 \times 2y^{-4}$ (f) $\frac{6y^{-2}}{3y^4}$

In questions **4–6** do not use a calculator.

4 Simplify and evaluate the following expressions:
(a) $3^3 \times 3^{-5}$ (b) $\frac{7^5 \times 7^{-2}}{7^4}$ (c) $27^{-\frac{1}{3}} \times 27^2$
(d) $(25^{\frac{1}{2}})^3$ (e) $(10^2)^{-\frac{3}{2}}$ (f) $\frac{2^0 \times 2^5}{2^{-4}}$

5 Evaluate the following expressions, giving your answer in standard form:
(a) $(2.3 \times 10^{-2}) \times (5 \times 10^8)$ (b) $(4 \times 10^{-3}) \times (3.1 \times 10^4)$
(c) $(2.8 \times 10^4) \div (7 \times 10^{-3})$ (d) $\frac{1.8 \times 10^5}{4 \times 10^3}$

6 Estimate the value of the following calculations:
(a) $878\,321 \times 0.004\,32$ (b) $0.002\,56 \times 0.078$
(c) $87.34 \div 0.002\,85$ (d) $0.009\,21 \div 42\,100\,000$

7 A meteorite of mass 2.4×10^6 kg lands on the Moon. The meteorite has a mass 3.06×10^{13} smaller than the Moon. Calculate the mass of the Moon.

Summary of key points

■ $x^0 = 1$ for all non-zero values of x.

■ $x^{-n} = \frac{1}{x^n}$ (where $x \neq 0$).

■ $x^{\frac{1}{n}} = \sqrt[n]{x}$

■ $x^{\frac{m}{n}} = (\sqrt[n]{x})^m$ or $x^{\frac{m}{n}} = \sqrt[n]{x^m}$

■ $x^n \times x^m = x^{n+m}$

■ $x^n \div x^m = x^{n-m}$ or $\frac{x^n}{x^m} = x^{n-m}$

■ $(x^n)^m = x^{n \times m}$

■ **Standard form can be used to make approximations and estimates.**

2 Proportion, estimating and accuracy

2.1 Finding proportionality rules from ratios

In Stage 1 you learned about direct and inverse proportion and ratios.

- **You can use ratios to find the rule connecting quantities that are in direct or inverse proportion to one another.**

Example 1

The distance travelled by a car is directly proportional to the amount of petrol used.
A car travels 35.7 km and uses 7 litres of petrol.

(a) Find a rule connecting the distance travelled, d, and the amount of petrol used, p.
(b) Find the distance that can be travelled by the car using 11 litres of petrol.

(a) The distance-to-petrol ratio is

$$35.7 : 7$$
$$\text{or } \frac{35.7}{7} = 5.1$$

The rule connecting distance travelled and petrol used is $d = 5.1p$.

(b) Using the rule, when $p = 11$ litres then $d = 5.1 \times 11 = 56.1$ km.

Example 2

The time taken to build a wall is inversely proportional to the number of bricklayers building the wall.
Three bricklayers take 6 hours to build a wall.
How long will it take four bricklayers to build a similar wall working at the same rate?

This information can be presented in a table:

$$\times \frac{4}{3}$$

No. of bricklayers	3	4
No. of hours	6	?

The number of bricklayers has been multiplied by $\frac{4}{3}$.
The number of hours taken is **inversely proportional** to the number of bricklayers. So to find the number of hours required we need to multiply 6 by the inverse of $\frac{4}{3}$:

$$\times \frac{4}{3}$$

No. of bricklayers	3	4
No. of hours	6	$4\frac{1}{2}$

$$\times \frac{3}{4}$$

So 4 bricklayers will take $6 \times \frac{3}{4} = 4\frac{1}{2}$ hours.

Exercise 2A   Links (*17C*) 17C

1 The mass of a book is directly proportional to the number of pages it contains.
A book with a mass of 0.8 kg contains 320 pages.
Calculate the mass of a similar book containing 220 pages.

2 The voltage V across a resistor is directly proportional to the current I flowing through it.
A current of 6.2 amperes produces a voltage of 10.9 volts.
(a) Find a rule connecting V and I.
(b) Calculate the voltage produced by a current of 4.3 amperes.

3 The circumference of a circle is directly proportional to its radius.
A circle has a radius of 6 cm and a circumference of 37.7 cm.
(a) Find a rule connecting the radius and circumference of a circle.
(b) Use your rule to find the circumference of a circle with a radius of 8 cm.

4 A football team wins a trophy in a competition.
The players in the team are each given a miniature replica of the trophy. The mass of the trophy is in direct proportion to its volume. The original trophy has a mass of 2.55 kg and a volume of 850 cm³.
(a) Find a rule connecting the volume of the trophy and its mass.
(b) The replica trophies has a volume of 425 cm³. Calculate the mass of a replica trophy.

5 A tree 6 metres high casts a shadow 4 metres long. The length of the shadow is directly proportional to the height of the tree.
(a) Find a rule connecting the length of the shadow and the height of the tree.
(b) Calculate the length of the shadow cast by a tree 9.6 metres high.
(c) Calculate the height of a tree that casts a shadow of 12.6 metres.

6 Two variables, x and y, are inversely proportional to each other. Complete the table for these variables:

x	4	6	
y	15		6

7 The number of drinks that can be poured from a bottle of cola is inversely proportional to the size of glass used.
Six drinks can be poured from a bottle of cola using 250 ml glasses. Drinks are poured from a similar bottle of cola using 300 ml glasses. Calculate the number of drinks that can be poured.

8 For rectangles of constant area the length of the rectangle is inversely proportional to the width of the rectangle.
A rectangle has sides of 15 cm and 12 cm. Calculate the width of a rectangle with the same area that is 10 cm long.

2.2 Exponential growth and decay

Example 3
A very famous mathematical problem asks the following question:
'If you place 1 grain of rice on the first square of a chessboard, 2 grains on the second square, 4 grains on the third square and so on, doubling each time, how many grains of rice will be placed on the 64th square?'

This is an example of exponential growth: the size of each new pile of rice is found by multiplying the number of grains in the previous pile by 2.
To find the answer you can of course use a calculator.
There are several methods you could use.

Method 1
You could simply use your calculator to work out

Square 1: 1
Square 2: $1 \times 2 = 2$
Square 3: $2 \times 2 = 4$
Square 4: $4 \times 2 = 8$
Square 5: $8 \times 2 = 16$
etc.

This method would work but would take a long time to get to an answer.

Method 2
Most scientific calculators allow you to repeat a calculation without having to enter the previous answer again, using `ANS` and `EXE` buttons.

Step 1:

Enter **1** **EXE**

This is the starting point of the problem.

Step 2:

Enter **ANS** **×** **2** **EXE**

This gives an answer of 2 on the display, which is the number of grains of rice on the second square.

Step 3:

Enter **EXE**

The display should show 4, the number of grains of rice on the third square.

Every time you press **EXE** the display will show the size of the next pile of rice, so all you need to do is press **EXE** 61 more times!

This method is an improvement on **method 1** but still relies on you not losing count.

Method 3

The problem can be written as

Square 1: 1	or 1×2^0
Square 2: 1×2	or 1×2^1
Square 3: $(1 \times 2) \times 2$	or 1×2^2
Square 4: $(1 \times 2 \times 2) \times 2$	or 1×2^3
Square 5: $(1 \times 2 \times 2 \times 2) \times 2$	or 1×2^4

$\vdots$

Square n: $1 \times 2^{n-1}$

So square $64 = 1 \times 2^{63}$ which you can enter on your calculator as

1 **×** **2** **x^y** **63** $= 9.22 \times 10^{18}$.

> In reality it would be impossible to do this problem with real grains of rice. For example, by the 32nd square you would need 2 147 483 648 grains of rice. If you counted 100 grains per minute it would take around 40 years to count this number of grains.

Example 4

A population of bacteria is reduced by $\frac{2}{3}$ every hour.
If the population starts with 5 000 000 bacteria, how many will remain after 6 hours?

After 1 h the number of bacteria will be

$5\,000\,000 \times \frac{1}{3}$

So after 6 h the number of bacteria will be

$5\,000\,000 \times (\frac{1}{3})^6 = 7000$

> As the accuracy of the data is given to 1 significant figure, the answer has been given to 1 significant figure also. You will find that in some questions you will need to consider the accuracy of your answer: e.g. for questions involving money, answers should be given to the nearest penny.

Exercise 2B

For each question in this exercise, remember to give your answers to an appropriate degree of accuracy.

1 In Example **3**, how many grains of rice would be placed on the
   (a) 8th square **(b)** 16th square?

2 A cell divides into 2 every hour. Assuming that no cells die, how many cells will there be after
   (a) 24 hours **(b)** 1 week?

3 The population of a village doubles every 5 years. The population in 1975 was 1365. What was the population in 2000?

4 The size of a coral reef is halving every 3 years. The coral reef is currently $1250\,000\,\text{m}^3$. How big will it be in 30 years' time if it continues to shrink at this rate?

5 A population of insects trebles every 4 days. Initially the population is 240. Assuming no insect dies, how many insects will there be after
   (a) 20 days **(b)** 32 days **(c)** 52 days?

6 The population of a particular type of fish is reduced by a disease. The population is reduced by a third every 3 months. The population of fish is 1.2×10^9. Assuming the disease continues to destroy fish at the same rate and no new fish join the population, how many fish will there be in the population after 2 years?

2.3 Using surds and π in calculations

Teaching reference:
pp 471–474, section 23.3

■ **A number written exactly using square roots is called a *surd*. For example, $\sqrt{3}$ and $2 - \sqrt{5}$ are in surd form.**

■ **Surds can be added, subtracted, multiplied and divided.**

$$\sqrt{a \times b} = \sqrt{a} \times \sqrt{b} \qquad \sqrt{\dfrac{a}{b}} = \dfrac{\sqrt{a}}{\sqrt{b}}$$

■ **Answers in surd form or in terms of π are exact answers.**

Example 5

(a) Simplify $\sqrt{20}$. (b) Simplify $\sqrt{\dfrac{18}{4}}$.

(a) $\begin{aligned}\sqrt{20} &= \sqrt{4 \times 5} \\ &= \sqrt{4} \times \sqrt{5} \\ &= 2\sqrt{5}\end{aligned}$

(b) $\sqrt{\dfrac{18}{4}} = \dfrac{\sqrt{18}}{\sqrt{4}} = \dfrac{\sqrt{9 \times 2}}{2} = \dfrac{\sqrt{9} \times \sqrt{2}}{2} = \dfrac{3}{2}\sqrt{2}$

Example 6

A square has an area of $12\,\text{cm}^2$.
Find the exact length of the side of the square.

Call the length of the side of the square l.

$$\text{Area of the square} = l^2$$
$$12 = l^2$$
$$\sqrt{12} = l$$
$$\sqrt{4 \times 3} = l$$
$$\sqrt{4} \times \sqrt{3} = l$$
$$2\sqrt{3}\,\text{cm} = l$$

Example 7

The shape below is made from a semicircle and a rectangle.
Calculate the exact area of the shape.

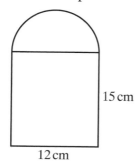

15 cm

12 cm

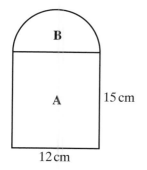

B

A   15 cm

12 cm

$$\text{Area } \mathbf{A} = 12 \times 15$$
$$= 180\,\text{cm}^2$$
$$\text{Area } \mathbf{B} = \frac{\pi \times 6^2}{2}$$
$$= \frac{\pi \times 36}{2}$$
$$= 18\pi\,\text{cm}^2$$
$$\text{Total area} = (180 + 18\pi)\,\text{cm}^2$$

Exercise 2C   Links (*23C*) 23C

Do not use a calculator for this exercise.

1   Simplify:

   (a) $\sqrt{28}$ **(b)** $\sqrt{45}$ **(c)** $\sqrt{8}$ **(d)** $\sqrt{27}$ **(e)** $\sqrt{6} \times \sqrt{10}$

   (f) $\sqrt{2} \times \sqrt{6}$ **(g)** $\sqrt{\dfrac{12}{9}}$ **(h)** $\sqrt{\dfrac{24}{16}}$ **(i)** $\sqrt{\dfrac{27}{25}}$

2   Find the exact value of x:
    (a) $x^2 = 20$ **(b)** $x^2 - 3 = 15$ **(c)** $2x^2 + 5 = x^2 + 17$

3 $ABCD$ is a rectangle.
    $AB = 2\sqrt{3}$, $BC = \sqrt{6}$.
    (a) Calculate the area of the rectangle.
    (b) Calculate the length of the diagonal AC.

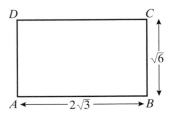

4   The diagram represents an isosceles triangle.

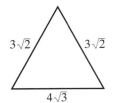

    (a) Calculate the vertical height of the triangle.
    (b) Calculate the area of the triangle.

5   Work out the area and circumference of a circle with a radius of 6 cm.

6   The area of a circle is $12\pi \text{ cm}^2$.
    (a) Calculate the radius of the circle.
    (b) Calculate the circumference of the circle.

2.4 Upper bounds and lower bounds

■ **If you make a measurement correct to a given unit the true value lies in a range that extends half a unit below and half a unit above the measurement.**

■ **The greatest lower bound and least upper bound are the minimum and maximum possible values of a measurement or calculation.**

Example 8

A rectangle has a length of 8.5 cm and width 2.3 cm, measured to the nearest 0.1 cm.
Work out

(a) the greatest lower bounds of the length and the width,
(b) the least upper bounds of the length and the width.

(a) The greatest lower bound of the length is 8.45 cm.
    The greatest lower bound of the width is 2.25 cm.
(b) The least upper bound of the length is 8.55 cm.
    The least upper bound of the width is 2.35 cm.

Exercise 2D   **Links (*12E, 12F, 23D*) 12E, 12F, 23D**

1   All these measurements are written to the nearest centimetre.
Write down the smallest and largest lengths they could be.
(a) 12 cm   (b) 10.02 m   (c) 6 cm
(d) 9.01 m   (e) 8.00 m

2   The distance between two towns is 23 km to the nearest
kilometre.
Write down the range of distances in which the true distance
must lie.

3   The numbers below are written correct to the numbers of
significant figures given in the brackets.
For each number write down the maximum and minimum
value it could be.
(a) 180 (2 s.f.)   (b) 530 100 (4 s.f.)
(c) 0.002 (1 s.f.)   (d) 0.0032 (2 s.f.)

4   Linford ran 100 m.
His time for the run was 12.3 seconds to the nearest tenth of a
second.
Write down the least upper bound and greatest lower bound
for his time.

5   A cuboid has dimensions of 2.4 cm, 4.5 cm and 6.8 cm to the
nearest 0.1 centimetre.
For each dimension write down
(a) the least upper bound
(b) the greatest lower bound.

2.5 Calculations involving upper and lower bounds

■   **When calculating using least upper bounds (LUB) and
greatest lower bounds (GLB), use this table to help you:**

Calculation	Result
LUB + LUB	LUB
GLB + GLB	GLB
LUB − GLB	LUB
GLB − LUB	GLB
LUB × LUB	LUB
GLB × GLB	GLB
LUB ÷ GLB	LUB
GLB ÷ LUB	GLB

Example 9

A rectangular lawn has sides measured as 4.3 m and 2.5 m to 1 d.p. Calculate the least upper bound and greatest lower bound of the perimeter of the garden.

The largest value for the perimeter is found from the longest possible sides:

$$2 \times (4.35 + 2.55) = 2 \times 6.9 = 13.8 \text{ m}$$

The least upper bound for the perimeter is 13.8 m.

The smallest value for the perimeter is found from the shortest possible sides:

$$2 \times (4.25 + 2.45) = 2 \times 6.7 = 13.4 \text{ m}$$

The greatest lower bound for the perimeter is 13.4 m.

Example 10

Pamela travels from Bedford to Manchester by car. She measures the distance as 179 miles to the nearest mile and uses 21.4 litres of petrol, to 1 d.p.
Calculate the least upper bound and greatest lower bound of the car's fuel economy in miles per litre.

Fuel economy is found by dividing the number of miles travelled by the number of litres of petrol used.
The greatest value for the fuel economy can be found by using the largest possible distance and the smallest amount of petrol:

$$\frac{179.5}{21.35} = 8.41 \text{ miles per litre (to 3 s.f.)}$$

The lowest value for the fuel economy can be found by using the smallest possible distance and the largest amount of petrol:

$$\frac{178.5}{21.45} = 8.32 \text{ miles per litre (to 3 s.f.)}$$

Exercise 2E   **Links** *(23E, 23F)* **23E, 23F**

Calculate the least upper bound and greatest lower bound for each of the quantities or calculations. The degree of accuracy for each measurement or number is given.

1   The area of a rectangle with sides 2.4 cm and 5.8 cm measured to the nearest millimetre.

2   The area of a circle with a radius of 5 cm measured to the nearest centimetre.

3   The length of the side of a rectangle with area 42.5 cm^2 correct to 1 d.p. and width 4.5 cm to the nearest millimetre.

4 The perimeter of a triangle with sides 12 cm, 11 cm and 17 cm measured to 2 s.f.

5 The average speed of a runner who runs a 200 m race in 23.2 seconds. The running track is measured to the nearest metre and the time to the nearest $\frac{1}{10}$ second. (Speed = distance ÷ time.)

6 The temperature range on a day when the minimum and maximum temperatures are recorded as $-3\,°C$ and $11\,°C$ to the nearest degree.

7 The circumference of a circle with a radius of 0.23 m measured to 2 d.p.

8 The density of a block of wood of mass 240 g to the nearest gram and volume 80 cm^3 correct to 1 s.f. (Density = mass/volume.)

9 $\dfrac{2.1 + 3.8}{4.5}$ all figures correct to 1 d.p.

10 $\dfrac{200(10 + 50)}{300}$ all figures correct to 1 s.f.

2.6 Errors

■ **The absolute error is the difference between the measured value and the notional value of a quantity.**

■ **The percentage error is found by converting the fraction $\dfrac{\text{absolute error}}{\text{notional value}}$ into a percentage.**

Example 11

A bag of toffees is labelled as weighing 250 g, but is found to have a weight of 262 g.

(a) Find the absolute error in the weight of the bag of toffees.
(b) Find the percentage error in the weight of the bag of toffees.

(a) The absolute error is $262 - 250 = 12$ g.

(b) The percentage error is $\dfrac{12}{250} \times 100\% = 4.8\%$.

> It does not matter whether this is +12 g or −12 g, the absolute error will still be 12 g.

Example 12

Find the maximum percentage error of a measurement of 8 cm to the nearest centimetre.

The least upper bound and greatest lower bound are 8.5 cm and 7.5 cm.
Taking either value gives an absolute error of 0.5 cm.

The percentage error $= \dfrac{0.5}{8} \times 100\% = 6.25\%$.

Exercise 2F   Links (*23G*) 23G

1   A packet of biscuits is labelled 400 g. The actual weight is
     found to be 386 g. Calculate the absolute and percentage error
     of the weight.

2   A length of fabric is labelled 3 m. Its actual length is found to
     be 3.12 m. Calculate the absolute and percentage error of the
     length.

3   The capacity of a petrol tank is given as 45 litres. When filled
     it is found to hold 45.8 litres. Calculate the absolute and
     percentage error of the capacity of the tank.

4   A curtain rail is measured as 1.8 m to the nearest 5 cm.
     Calculate the maximum possible absolute error and maximum
     percentage error of the length of the curtain rail.

5   The distance between two villages is measured as 3.2 miles to
     the nearest $\frac{1}{10}$ mile. Calculate the maximum percentage error
     in the distance between the two villages.

6   A triangle has a base of 6 cm and perpendicular height of
     10 cm measured to the nearest centimetre. Calculate the
     maximum possible absolute error and maximum percentage
     error of the area of the triangle.

7   1.414 is often used as an approximation for $\sqrt{2}$. Calculate the
     maximum percentage error in using this approximation for $\sqrt{2}$.
     (Use the value for $\sqrt{2}$ given on your calculator as a more
     correct value.)

8   The radius of a circle is measured as 3.4 cm correct to 2 s.f.
     Calculate the maximum possible absolute error and maximum
     percentage error in
     (a) the radius of the circle
     (b) the area of the circle.

Exercise 2G   Mixed questions

1   The voltage, V, across a resistor is directly proportional to the
     current, I, flowing through it.
     A current of 2.4 amperes produces a voltage of 6.0 volts.
     (a) Find a rule connecting V and I.
     (b) Calculate the voltage produced by a current of 9 amperes.
     (c) Calculate the size of current required to produce a voltage
          of 8.5 volts.

2 Two variables, a and b, are inversely proportional to each other. Complete the table for these variables:

a	25	15	
b	36		100

3 The population of a village trebles every 4 years. The population was 682 in 1960. What was the population of the village in
(a) 1972 **(b)** 1988?

4 Simplify, without using a calculator:

(a) $\sqrt{20}$ **(b)** $\sqrt{63}$ **(c)** $\sqrt{6} \times \sqrt{8}$ **(d)** $\sqrt{\dfrac{12}{16}}$

5 A square has an area of $27\,\text{cm}^2$. Calculate the exact length of a side of the square.

6 A window is made in the shape of a rectangle with a semicircular top, with dimensions as shown on the diagram. Calculate an exact value for the area of the glass.

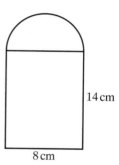

14 cm

8 cm

7 The lengths in question **6** were measured to the nearest 0.1 cm. Work out
(a) the greatest lower bounds of the length and width of the rectangle,
(b) the least upper bounds of the length and width of the rectangle.

8 Calculate the least upper bound and greatest lower bound of the average speed of a runner who runs a 100 m race in 13.4 seconds. The running track was measured to the nearest metre and the time recorded to 1 d.p.

9 An estimate of a calculation was made by rounding all numbers to 1 s.f.

The estimate was $\dfrac{300\,(40 \times 50)}{200}$.

Calculate the least upper bound and greatest lower bound of the estimate.

10 The capacity of a petrol tank is given as 60 litres. When filled it is found to be 62.3 litres. Calculate the absolute error and percentage error of the capacity of the tank.

11 A newborn baby is weighed. Her weight to the nearest 10 g is 1.68 kg. Calculate the maximum percentage error in the weight of the baby.

Summary of key points

- You can use ratios to find the rule connecting quantities that are in direct or inverse proportion to one another.

- A number written exactly as a square root is called a surd.

- Surds can be added, subtracted, multiplied and divided.

$$\sqrt{a \times b} = \sqrt{a} \times \sqrt{b} \qquad \sqrt{\frac{a}{b}} = \frac{\sqrt{a}}{\sqrt{b}}$$

- Answers in surd form or in terms of π are exact answers.

- If you make a measurement correct to a given unit the true value lies in a range that extends half a unit below and half a unit above the measurement.

- The greatest lower bound and least upper bound are the minimum and maximum possible values of a measurement or calculation.

- When calculating using least upper bounds (LUB) and greatest lower bounds (GLB) use this table to help you:

Calculation	Result
LUB + LUB	LUB
GLB + GLB	GLB
LUB − GLB	LUB
GLB − LUB	GLB
LUB × LUB	LUB
GLB × GLB	GLB
LUB ÷ GLB	LUB
GLB ÷ LUB	GLB

- The absolute error is the difference between the measured value and the notional value of a quantity.

- The percentage error is found by converting the fraction $\frac{\text{absolute error}}{\text{notional value}}$ into a percentage.

3 Algebra: graphs

3.1 Straight line graphs

- An intercept is a point at which a line cuts the y-axis or the x-axis.

- The equation of a straight line $y = mx + c$ has a gradient m and its intercept on the y-axis is $(0, c)$.

- Lines with the same gradient (m) are parallel.

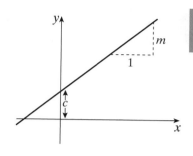

Example 1

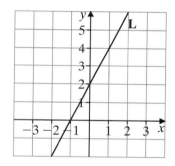

(a) Work out the equation of the line **L** drawn above.

A second line **M** is parallel to **L** and passes through the point $(3, 5)$.

(b) Work out the equation of the second line **M**.

(a) The equation of the line **L** will be $y = mx + c$, where m is the gradient and c is the intercept with the y-axis.
From the graph we can read off c to be 2 units and we can work out m to be 2.
So the equation of the line **L** is $y = 2x + 2$.

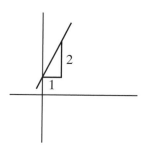

(b) Since the line **M** is parallel to line **L** then the gradient of **M** is equal to the gradient of **L**.
So the equation of **M** will be

$$y = 2x + k$$

where k is the intercept of this line with the y-axis.
We can work out the value of k by substituting because we know that this line passes through the point $(3, 5)$.
So when $x = 3$ then $y = 5$.
Substituting these values into $y = 2x + k$ gives

$$5 = 2 \times 3 + k$$
or $$5 = 6 + k$$

So $k = -1$.
So the equation of the line **M** is $y = 2x - 1$.

Example 2

The equation of a straight line is

$$2x + 3y = 18$$

(a) Write the equation of the line in the form $y = mx + c$.
(b) State the values of the gradient and intercept with the y-axis for this line.
(c) Sketch the line.

(a) Rearranging the equation of the line:

$$2x + 3y = 18$$
so $$3y = -2x + 18$$

so $$y = \frac{-2x}{3} + \frac{18}{3}$$

so $$y = \frac{-2x}{3} + 6 \qquad \text{which is in the required form.}$$

(b) The gradient of the line is m so this is $-\frac{2}{3}$.
The intercept with the y-axis is 6.
(c) The sketch of the line is:

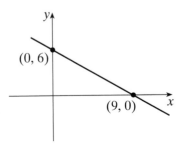

because it goes through $(0, 6)$ with gradient $-\frac{2}{3}$.

Exercise 3A   **Links 7A, 7B**

1   Draw each of these graphs:
   (a) $y = 2x - 3$ **(b)** $y = \frac{1}{2}x + 5$ **(c)** $y = 12 - 3x$
   (d) $x + 3y = 6$ **(e)** $4x - 3y = 12$ **(f)** $6y + 4x = 30$
   In each case, find:
   (i) the gradient   **(ii)** the intercept with the y-axis.

2

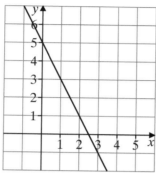

   (a) Work out the equation of the line above.
   A second line is parallel to the line drawn above and passes
   through the point $(-1, 1)$.
   (b) Work out the equation of the second line.

3   Work out the gradient and the intercept on the y-axis of the
   straight line
$$4y - 9x = 24$$

4   A straight line passes through the points $(1, 1)$ and $(4, 10)$.
   Work out the equation of this straight line.

5   The points A, B, C and D are the four vertices of a rectangle.
   The coordinates of these four points are:
   $A(1, 1)$ $B(1, 3)$ $C(5, 3)$ $D(5, 1)$
   Work out the equations of the two diagonals AC and BD of
   the rectangle.

6

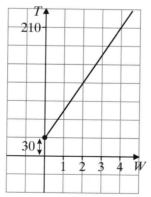

   The graph above shows the time, T minutes, required to cook
   a joint of meat weighing W kg.
   T is given by the formula $T = mW + c$. Work out the values of m and c.

3.2 Solving quadratic equations graphically

- A quadratic function is one in which the highest power of x is x^2.

- The general equation of a quadratic graph is
  $y = ax^2 + bx + c$.

- The solutions of a quadratic equation are the values of x where the graph cuts the x-axis.

Teaching reference:
pp 368–369, section 18.1

Example 3

(a) For values of x from -3 to 2, draw the graph of
    $y = 3x^2 + 5x - 1$.

(b) Use your graph to find the approximate solutions to the equation

$$3x^2 + 5x - 1 = 0$$

(c) Use your graph to find the approximate solution to the equation

$$3x^2 + 5x - 6 = 0$$

(a) Set up the table of values:

x	-3	-2	-1	0	1	2
$3x^2$	27	12	3	0	3	12
$+5x$	-15	-10	-5	0	5	10
-1	-1	-1	-1	-1	-1	-1
y	11	1	-3	-1	7	21

So the graph is:

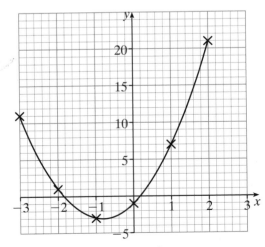

The solutions of the equation $3x^2 + 5x - 1 = 0$ occur where the graph $y = 3x^2 + 5x - 1$ crosses the x-axis, i.e. where $y = 0$.

From the graph we can see that the approximate solutions are

$x = -1.8$ and 0.2

correct to one decimal place.

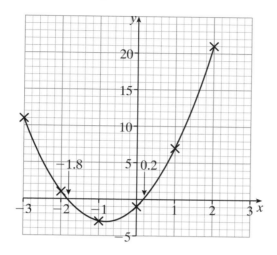

(c) To solve

$$3x^2 + 5x - 6 = 0$$

we need to rearrange to

$$3x^2 + 5x - 1 - 5 = 0$$

i.e. $3x^2 + 5x - 1 = 5$

The solutions occur when the graph of

$y = 3x^2 + 5x - 1$

crosses the line $y = 5$.

i.e.

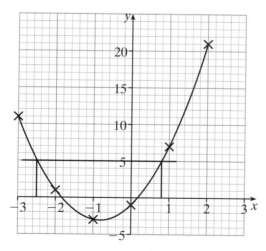

$x = 0.8$ and $x = -2.5$.

Example 4

The graphs of

$$y = x^2 \quad \text{and} \quad y = 7 - x$$

are drawn here on the same axes:

Use these graphs to find approximate solutions to the equation

$$x^2 + x - 7 = 0$$

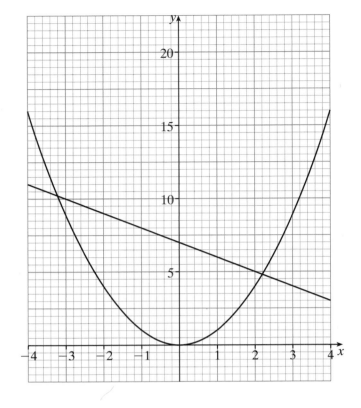

The points where the two graphs cross are the points where

$$x^2 = 7 - x$$

but rearranging this equation gives

$$x^2 + x - 7 = 0$$

From the graphs, the two meet at the x-values of

$$x = 2.2 \text{ and } -3.2$$

correct to one decimal place.

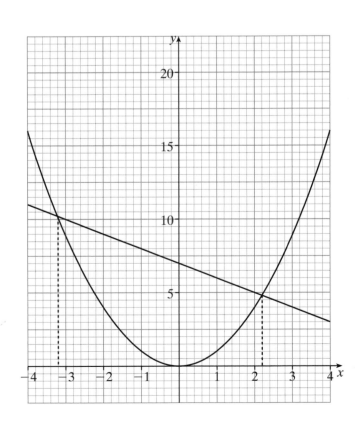

Exercise 3B   Links 18E

1 **(a)** Complete the table of values for $y = 2x^2 - 1$:

x	-3	-2	-1	0	1	2	3
y	17				1	7	

  (b) On a grid draw the graph of $y = 2x^2 - 1$.

  (c) Use your graph to
   (i)   solve the equation $2x^2 - 1 = 0$,
   (ii) find the value of y when $x = 2.5$,
   (iii) find the values of x when $y = 12.5$.

2 **(a)** For values of x from -4 to 4, draw the graph of

$$y = 2x^2 - 3x - 8$$

  (b) Use your graph to find approximate solutions to the equation

$$2x^2 - 3x - 8 = 0$$

3 **(a)** On the same axes, draw the graphs of $y = x^2$ and $y = 3x - 1$.

  (b) Use your graphs to find approximate solutions to the equation

$$x^2 - 3x + 1 = 0$$

4 **(a)** For values of x from -4 to 4, draw the graph of

$$y = 3 + x - x^2$$

  (b) Use your graph to find approximate solutions to the equation

$$3 + x - x^2 = 0$$

5

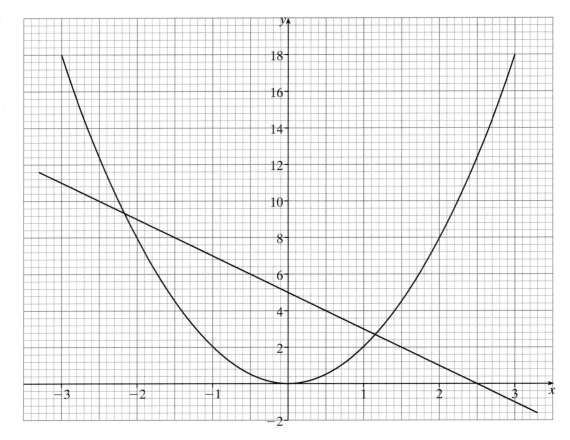

The graphs of $y = 2x^2$ and $y = 5 - 2x$ are drawn on the same axes above.

Use the graphs to find approximate solutions to the equation

$$2x^2 + 2x - 5 = 0$$

3.3 Cubic, reciprocal, exponential and trigonometric graphs

■ A cubic function is one in which the highest power of x is x^3.

■ The number with x^3 is called the coefficient of x^3.

■ The graph of a general cubic is like this if the coefficient of x^3 is positive:

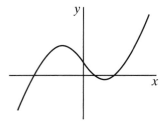

and like this when the coefficient of x^3 is negative:

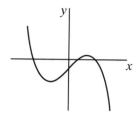

- To find the reciprocal of a number or expression divide it into 1.

- The graph of $y = \dfrac{1}{x}$ is like this:

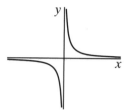

- Functions such as 2^x or 3^x are called *exponential* functions.

- The graph of $y = a^x (a \neq 0)$ is like this:

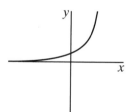

- The graph of $y = \sin x°$ is like this:

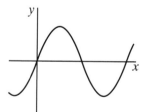

- The graph of $y = \cos x°$ is like this:

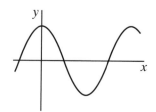

Example 5

On the same axes draw the graphs of $y = x^3 + 1$ and $y = \dfrac{3}{x}$ for values of x from -3 to 3.

The tables of values are

x	$y = x^3 + 1$	$y = \dfrac{3}{x}$
-3	$-27 + 1 = -26$	$\dfrac{3}{-3} = -1$
-2	$-8 + 1 = -7$	$\dfrac{3}{-2} = -1.5$
-1	$-1 + 1 = 0$	$\dfrac{3}{-1} = -3$
0	$0 + 1 = 1$	discontinuity
1	$1 + 1 = 2$	$\dfrac{3}{1} = 3$
2	$8 + 1 = 9$	$\dfrac{3}{2} = 1.5$
3	$27 + 1 = 28$	$\dfrac{3}{3} = 1$

For $\dfrac{3}{x}$ it is important to look at some values for x close to and either side of 0.

We look at:

$$x = \frac{1}{2} \qquad \frac{3}{x} = 6, \qquad x = \frac{1}{3} \qquad \frac{3}{x} = 9, \qquad x = \frac{1}{4} \qquad \frac{3}{x} = 12$$

$$x = -\frac{1}{2} \qquad \frac{3}{x} = -6, \qquad x = -\frac{1}{3} \qquad \frac{3}{x} = -9, \qquad x = -\frac{1}{4} \qquad \frac{3}{x} = -12$$

So the two graphs are

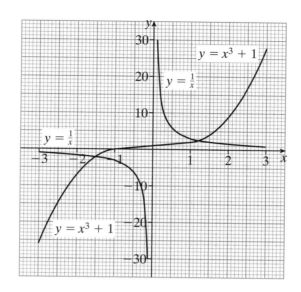

Example 6

Fiona and Rick bought a flat for £60 000 in July 2000.
They anticipate that the value of the flat will increase by 5% each year.
Draw the graph of the anticipated value of the flat from July 2000 to July 2010.

The value of the flat in July 2001 is $60\,000 + 5\%$ of $60\,000$

or $\qquad 60\,000 + 0.05 \times 60\,000 = 60\,000 \times 1.05$

The value of the flat in July 2002 is

value in 2001×1.05
i.e. $\quad 60\,000 \times 1.05 \times 1.05$
i.e. $\quad 60\,000 \times 1.05^2$

n years after July 2000 the anticipated value of the flat will be

value of flat $= 60\,000 \times (1.05)^n$

This give a table of values:

July	n	Anticipated value of the flat (£)
200	0	60 000
2001	1	$60\,000 \times 1.05 = 63\,000$
2002	2	$60\,000 \times (1.05)^2 = 66\,150$
2003	3	69 457.50
2004	4	72 930.375
2005	5	76 576.89
2006	6	80 405.74
2007	7	84 426.03
2008	8	88 647.33
2009	9	93 079.69
2010	10	97 733.68

Plotting the anticipated values against year gives the graph

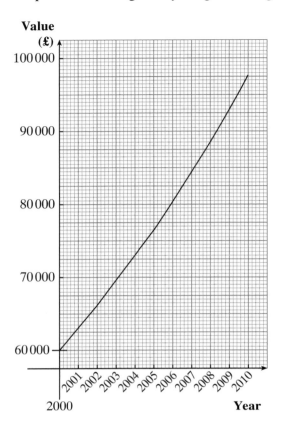

Example 7

$y = 2^x$

(a) Complete the table of values for $y = 2^x$ for values of x from -3 to 3:

x	-3	-2	-1	0	1	2	3
y							

(b) Hence draw the graph of $y = 2^x$.

(a) $2^{-3} = \dfrac{1}{8} = 0.125$ $2^{-2} = \dfrac{1}{4} = 0.25$ $2^{-1} = \dfrac{1}{2} = 0.5$ $2^0 = 1$

   $2^1 = 2$ $2^2 = 4$ $2^3 = 8$

so the table is

x	-3	-2	-1	0	1	2	3
y	0.125	0.25	0.5	1	2	4	8

(b) Hence the graph is

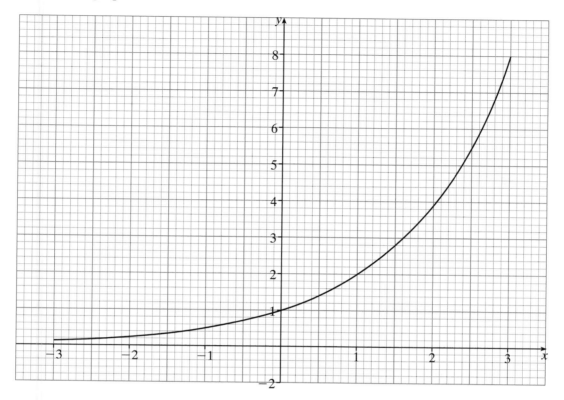

Example 8

For values of x from $0°$ to $360°$, sketch the graphs of

(a) $y = \sin x°$ (b) $y = 2\sin x°$

(a)

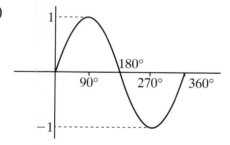

> You should know this shape but can check it: $\sin 0° = 0$, $\sin 45° = 0.7$, $\sin 90° = 1$.

(b) You should know that $y = 2\sin x$ will be 'double $\sin x$' in the vertical direction, so its graph is:

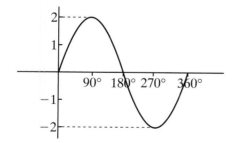

Example 9

The diagram represents a sketch of part of the graph of

$$y = pq^x \qquad q > 0$$

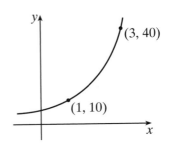

The graph passes through the points (1, 10) and (3, 40).

(a) Work out the values of p and q
(b) Work out the value of y when
    (i) $x = 4$ (ii) $x = -2$
(c) Work out the value of x when $y = 320$.

(a) Substituting into $y = pq^x$ when $x = 1$ gives

$$10 = pq^1 \quad \text{or} \quad pq = 10$$

Substituting into $y = pq^x$ when $x = 3$ gives

$$40 = pq^3 \quad \text{or} \quad pq^3 = 40$$

$$pq^3 = 40 \qquad pq = 10$$

Dividing these equations gives

$$\frac{pq^3}{pq} = \frac{40}{10}$$

$$q^2 = 4 \qquad q = \sqrt{4} = \pm 2$$

Since $q > 0 \qquad q = 2$.

Using $10 = pq$, with $q = 2$

$$pq = 10$$
$$p \times 2 = 10 \qquad p = 5$$

So $p = 5 \qquad q = 2$.

(b) The equation is

$$y = 5 \times 2^x \qquad 5 \times 2^x$$

(i) When $x = 4 \qquad y = 5 \times 2^4$
$$= 5 \times 16 = 80.$$

(ii) When $x = -2 \qquad y = 5 \times 2^{-2}$
$$= 5 \times \tfrac{1}{4} = \tfrac{5}{4} \text{ (or } 1.25\text{)}.$$

(c) The equation is

$$320 = 5 \times 2^x$$

$$2^x = \frac{320}{5} = 64$$

But $2^6 = 2 \times 2 \times 2 \times 2 \times 2 \times 2 = 64$

so $x = 6$.

Exercise 3C   **Links 13H, 13J, 18B, 18C**

1 Here is a list of sketches of graphs and a list of equations.
Match the equations to the graphs.

Curves   **Equations**

A 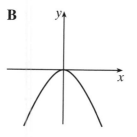   D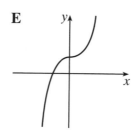

$y = \cos x$ $y = 5^x$

B 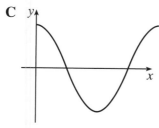   E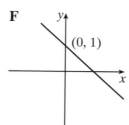

$y = x^3 + 2$ $y = \dfrac{5}{x}$

C   F

$y = -x^2$ $y = 1 - x$

2 On the same axes and for values of x from -3 to 3, plot the
graphs of

$$y = x^3 + x \qquad \text{and} \qquad y = \frac{10}{x}$$

3 Sketch the graph of $y = \cos x°$ for values of x from $0°$ to $360°$.

4 Afzal bought a new car for £12 000.
The value of the car depreciates by 15% each year.
Draw a graph of the value of the car from new until it is
6 years old.

5 On separate axes, sketch the graphs of
(a) $y = \sin x°$ for values of x from $0°$ to $360°$
(b) $y = 3 \sin x°$ for values of x from $-180°$ to $180°$
(c) $y = \cos x°$ for values of x from $0°$ to $360°$
(d) $y = 3 \cos x°$ for values of x from $0°$ to $360°$.

6 The cost of hiring a holiday villa for a month is £2000.
The cost is fixed and does not depend on how many people
hire the villa.
A group of people hire the villa for a month and share the
cost equally.
Sketch the graph of the **cost per person** as the number of
people in the group varies from 1 to 10.

7 On the same axes, and for values of x from -3 to 3, draw the
graphs of
(i) $y = 3^x$ and (ii) $y = 2^{-x}$.

8 Draw the graph of $y = \dfrac{1}{x+1}$.

9 The diagram shows the accurate plot of the graph
of a trigonometric function for values of x from
$0°$ to $1440°$.
Work out the equation of this graph.

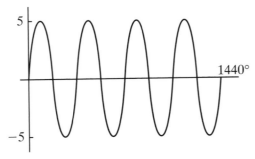

10 Sketch the graph of $y = (x-1)^3$.

11 (a) Draw the graph of
$$y = 2x^2 + 3x - 2$$
for values of x from -3 to 3.

(b) Use your graph to solve the equations
(i) $2x^2 + 3x - 2 = 0$
(ii) $2x^2 + 3x - 5 = 0$.
On the same axis, draw the graph of
$$y = x + 1$$

(c) Use your graphs to solve the equation
$$2x^2 + 3x - 2 = x + 1.$$

(d) Explain why the solutions to the equation
$$2x^2 + 3x - 2 = x + 1$$
are also the solutions to the equation
$$2x^2 + 2x - 3 = 0$$

12 The sketch shows part of the graph of $y = px^q$.

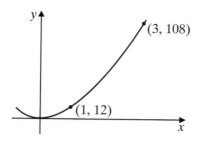

The curve passes through the points (1, 12) and (3, 108).
(a) Work out the values of p and q.
(b) Work out the value of y when
    (i) $x = 4$ **(ii)** $x = -1$.

13 The diagram shows a sketch of part of the curve

$$y = \cos x°$$

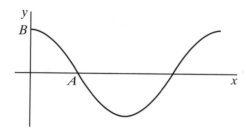

Write down the coordinates of the points A and B.

14 Here is a sketch of the graph of $y = \sin x°$ for values of x between $0°$ and $360°$.

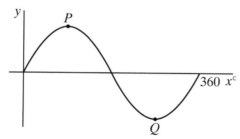

Write down the coordinates of the points
(a) P **(b)** Q.

15 The equation of a curve is

$$y = pq^x \qquad q > 0$$

The points (1, 10) and (3, 250) lie on the curve.
(a) Work out the values of p and q.
(b) Sketch the graph of the curve.
(c) Work out the value of y when
    (i) $x = -2$ **(ii)** $x = 2$
(d) Work out the value of x when $y = 1250$.

Summary of key points

■ An intercept is a point at which a line cuts the y-axis or the x-axis.

■ The equation of a straight line $y = mx + c$ has a gradient m and its intercept on the y-axis is $(0, c)$.

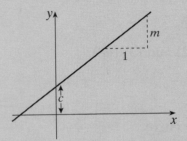

■ Lines with the same gradient (m) are parallel.

■ A quadratic function is one in which the highest power of x is x^2.

■ The general equation of a quadratic graph is $y = ax^2 + bx + c$.

■ The solutions of a quadratic equation are the values of x where the graph cuts the x-axis.

■ A cubic function is one in which the highest power of x is x^3.

■ The number with x^3 is called the coefficient of x^3.

■ The graph of a general cubic is like this if the coefficient of x^3 is positive:

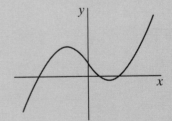

and like this when the coefficient of x^3 is negative:

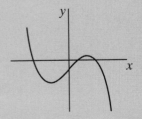

■ To find the reciprocal of a number or expression divide it into 1.

■ The graph of $y = \dfrac{1}{x}$ is like this:

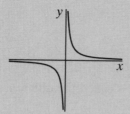

■ Functions such as 2^x or 3^x are called *exponential* functions.

■ The graph of $y = a^x$ $(a \neq 0)$ is like this:

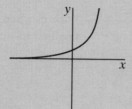

■ The graph of $y = \sin x°$ is like this:

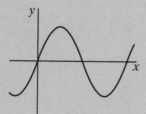

■ The graph of $y = \cos x°$ is like this:

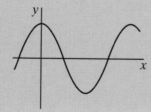

4 Working with algebra

4.1 Multiplying bracketed expressions

Teaching reference:
pp 196–198, section 10.10

■ $(e+f)(g+h) = e(g+h) + f(g+h)$
$$= eg + eh + fg + fh$$

■ **In general:** $(x+a)^2 = x^2 + 2ax + a^2$
$$(x-a)^2 = x^2 - 2ax + a^2$$
$$(x+a)(x-a) = x^2 - a^2 \quad\text{—— This is called the difference of two squares.}$$

Example 1
Expand and simplify $(x+4)(x+7)$.

$(x+4)(x+7) = x(x+7) + 4(x+7)$
$= x \times x + x \times 7 + 4 \times x + 4 \times 7$ —— With practice, you should not need
$= x^2 + 7x + 4x + 28$ this line of working.
$= x^2 + 11x + 28$

Example 2
Expand and simplify $(x-6)^2$.

$(x-6)^2 = x(x-6) - 6(x-6)$
$= x^2 - 6x - 6x + 36$ —— Notice that the last term is $-6 \times -6 = +36$.
$= x^2 - 12x + 36$

Example 3
Expand and simplify $(x+4)(x-4)$.

$(x+4)(x-4) = x(x-4) + 4(x-4)$
$= x^2 - 4x + 4x - 16$
$= x^2 - 16$

Example 4
Expand and simplify $(2x-5)(4x+3)$.

$(2x-5)(4x+3) = 2x(4x+3) - 5(4x+3)$
$= 2x \times 4x + 2x \times 3 - 5 \times 4x - 5 \times 3$ —— With practice, you should not
$= 8x^2 + 6x - 20x - 15$ need this line of working.
$= 8x^2 - 14x - 15$

Example 5
Expand $(3x+5)(2y-1)$.

$(3x+5)(2y-1) = 3x(2y-1) + 5(2y-1)$
$= 6xy - 3x + 10y - 5$

You cannot simplify this answer.

Exercise 4A Links 10J, 10K, 10L, 10M

1 Expand and simplify:
- **(a)** $(x + 3)(x + 5)$
- **(b)** $(x + 4)(x + 3)$
- **(c)** $(x + 2)(x + 8)$
- **(d)** $(x + 4)(x - 1)$
- **(e)** $(x - 6)(x + 3)$
- **(f)** $(x + 6)(x - 4)$
- **(g)** $(x - 3)(x - 9)$
- **(h)** $(x - 8)(x + 5)$
- **(i)** $(x - 1)(x - 6)$
- **(j)** $(x - 8)(x + 8)$
- **(k)** $(x - 6)(x - 2)$
- **(l)** $(x - 12)(x + 12)$

2 Expand:
- **(a)** $(a + 4)(b + 5)$
- **(b)** $(c + 7)(d - 3)$
- **(c)** $(p - 2)(q - 3)$
- **(d)** $(x - 5)(y + 7)$
- **(e)** $(a - 4)(t - 9)$
- **(f)** $(b + 5)(c - 8)$

3 Expand and simplify:
- **(a)** $(x + 4)^2$
- **(b)** $(x - 1)^2$
- **(c)** $(x + 7)^2$
- **(d)** $(x - 9)^2$

4 Expand and simplify where possible:
- **(a)** $(3x + 2)(x - 3)$
- **(b)** $(2x - 7)(3x + 2)$
- **(c)** $(4x - 5)(2x - 3)$
- **(d)** $(2x - 7)(y + 2)$
- **(e)** $(5x - 2)(2x - 7)$
- **(f)** $(5x + 6)(2y - 1)$
- **(g)** $(3x + 7)(3x - 7)$
- **(h)** $(3x + 9)(4x + 5)$
- **(i)** $(5x - 9)(5x + 9)$
- **(j)** $(2x + 3)^2$
- **(k)** $(3x - 5)^2$
- **(l)** $(5x + 1)^2$
- **(m)** $(7x - 2)^2$
- **(n)** $(2x + y)(5x + 7y)$
- **(o)** $(4x + 4y)(2x - 3y)$
- **(p)** $(7x - 3y)(2x - 5y)$
- **(q)** $(5x + 7y)(5x - 7y)$
- **(r)** $(4x - y)^2$
- **(s)** $(9x - 5y)(2x + 3y)$
- **(t)** $(3x + 5y)^2$
- **(u)** $(9x + 2y)(9x - 2y)$
- **(v)** $(8x - 3y)^2$

5 Expand and simplify:
- **(a)** $9 + (x - 3)(x + 5)$
- **(b)** $(4x + 3)(x - 2) + 5x - 2$
- **(c)** $(x + 1)(x - 3) + (x - 8)(x - 4)$
- **(d)** $(x + 7)(x - 3) - (x - 4)(x + 8)$
- **(e)** $(x + 6)^2 + (x - 1)^2$
- **(f)** $(x + 7)^2 - (x - 4)^2$
- **(g)** $(x + 5)^2 - (x - 5)^2$
- **(h)** $(5e + 3)^2 - 25e^2$
- **(i)** $(3x - 4)(3x + 4) - (3x - 4)^2$
- **(j)** $(3x + 1)^2 + 5(2x - 3)$
- **(k)** $(5x - 2)^2 - 3(2x - 1)$
- **(l)** $(2x - 5)(2x + 5) - (3x^2 - 25)$

4.2 Factorizing quadratic expressions

- Factorizing is the reverse process to expanding brackets.
- A quadratic expression has the form $ax^2 + bx + c$, where $a \neq 0$.
  - the coefficient of x^2 is a
  - the coefficient of x is b
  - the constant term is c.

Teaching reference:
(*pp 187–188, 371–372, 374–376, sections 10.3, 20.7, 20.81*)

Example 6

Factorize $4x^2 - 7x$.

$$4x^2 - 7x = x(4x - 7)$$

x is a common factor of $4x^2$ and $7x$.
So it can be taken outside the brackets.

Example 7

Factorize completely $10x^2 + 15x$.

$$10x^2 + 15x = 5x(2x + 3)$$

The expression has been completely factorized, because the terms inside the brackets, $2x$ and 3, do not have a common factor.

> $10x^2 + 15x = 5(2x^2 + 3x)$ and $10x^2 + 15x = x(10x + 15)$ but in each case the terms inside the brackets have a common factor and so the expression has not been completely factorized.

Example 8

Factorize $x^2 + 6x - 7$.

In other words, find two bracketed expressions which have a product of $x^2 + 6x - 7$.

The factors must be either:

$$(x + 7)(x - 1) \quad \text{or} \quad (x - 7)(x + 1)$$

$$x^2 + 6x - 7 = (x + 7)(x - 1)$$

The first term in each bracket must be x.
-7 tells you that the signs in the brackets are different.
1 and 7 are the only factors of 7.

Expand the brackets to find which pair has a product of $x^2 + 6x - 7$.

Example 9

Factorize $x^2 + 11x + 18$.
The factors must be one of these pairs:

$$(x + 1)(x + 18), (x + 2)(x + 9), (x + 3)(x + 6)$$

$+18$ tells you that the signs in the brackets are the same.
$+11x$ tells you that both the signs are $+$.
The pairs of factors of 18 are 1×18, 2×9 and 3×6.

$$x^2 + 11x + 12 = (x + 2)(x + 9)$$

Expand the brackets until you find the pair which has a product of $x^2 + 11x + 18$.

■ $x^2 - a^2 = (x + a)(x - a)$ ———————— This is called the difference of two squares.

Example 10

Factorize $x^2 - 49$.

$$x^2 - 49 = (x + 7)(x - 7)$$

Example 11

Factorize $6x^2 - 11x + 4$.

The factors must be one of these pairs:

$(6x - 1)(x - 4),$ $\quad$ $(6x - 2)(x - 2),$ $\quad$ $(6x - 4)(x - 1),$

$(3x - 1)(2x - 4),$ $\quad$ $(3x - 2)(2x - 2),$ $\quad$ $(3x - 4)(2x - 1)$

$6x^2 - 11x + 4 = (3x - 4)(2x - 1)$

$+4$ tells you that the signs in the brackets are the same.
$-11x$ tells you that both the signs are $-$.
The first terms in the brackets must be $6x$ and x or $3x$ and $2x$.
The pairs of factors of 4 are 1×4 and 2×2.
Expand the brackets until you find the pair which has a product of $x^2 - 11x + 4$.

Exercise 4B

Links 10C, 20I, 20J

1 Factorize each of these expressions:
- **(a)** $3x^2 + 5x$
- **(b)** $9x^2 - 12$
- **(c)** $x^2 - 2x$
- **(d)** $21x^2 + 7$
- **(e)** $ax^2 - 5a$
- **(f)** $bx^2 + 3x$
- **(g)** $7x^2 - 28py$
- **(h)** $ax^2 + bx$
- **(i)** $6x^2 - 8y$
- **(j)** $ax^2 + ay$
- **(k)** $8ax^2 - 4by$
- **(l)** $x - 5x^2$

2 Factorize each of these expressions completely:
- **(a)** $5x^2 + 10x$
- **(b)** $9x^2 - 6x$
- **(c)** $12x^2 - 4x$
- **(d)** $15x^2 + 10x$
- **(e)** $ax^2 - 4ax$
- **(f)** $3x^2 + 6bx$
- **(g)** $cx^2 - 2cx$
- **(h)** $ax^2 + ax$
- **(i)** $x^2y + xy^2$
- **(j)** $12xy^2 - 8y$
- **(k)** $8x^2 + 12xy$
- **(l)** $2x^2y^2 - 5xy$
- **(m)** $6x^2y + 15xy$
- **(n)** $10xy^2 - 8x^2y$
- **(o)** $6bx^2 + 3bx$

3 Factorize each of these quadratic expressions:
- **(a)** $x^2 + 4x + 3$
- **(b)** $x^2 - 2x - 3$
- **(c)** $x^2 - 3x + 2$
- **(d)** $x^2 - 6x - 7$
- **(e)** $x^2 - 6x + 5$
- **(f)** $x^2 + 12x + 11$
- **(g)** $x^2 + 2x + 1$
- **(h)** $x^2 - 10x - 11$
- **(i)** $x^2 - 8x + 16$
- **(j)** $x^2 - 7x + 6$
- **(k)** $x^2 - 4$
- **(l)** $x^2 - 9x + 20$
- **(m)** $x^2 - x - 20$
- **(n)** $x^2 + 6x + 9$
- **(o)** $x^2 - 64$
- **(p)** $x^2 - 20x + 100$
- **(q)** $x^2 + 3x - 10$
- **(r)** $x^2 - 11x - 12$
- **(s)** $x^2 + 8x + 15$
- **(t)** $x^2 - 9x + 14$
- **(u)** $x^2 + x - 30$
- **(v)** $x^2 - 121$
- **(w)** $x^2 + 10x + 25$
- **(x)** $x^2 - 3x - 28$

4 Factorize each of these quadratic expressions:
- **(a)** $3x^2 - 4x + 1$
- **(b)** $2x^2 - 50$
- **(c)** $2x^2 + 5x - 3$
- **(d)** $3x^2 - 18x + 21$
- **(e)** $5x^2 - 12x + 7$
- **(f)** $5x^2 - 20$
- **(g)** $9x^2 + 12x + 4$
- **(h)** $7x^2 - 35x + 42$
- **(i)** $8x^2 + 18x - 5$
- **(j)** $5x^2 + 28x - 12$
- **(k)** $4x^2 - 40x + 100$
- **(l)** $9x^2 - 16$
- **(m)** $9x^2 - 24x + 16$
- **(n)** $6x^2 - 13x - 8$
- **(o)** $6x^2 + 9x - 15$
- **(p)** $49x^2 - 9$
- **(q)** $12x^2 - 23x + 10$
- **(r)** $20x^2 - 60x + 45$
- **(s)** $15x^2 + 11x - 12$
- **(t)** $28x^2 - 7$
- **(u)** $14x^2 - 9x - 18$
- **(v)** $81x^2 - 64$
- **(w)** $20x^2 + 32x - 21$
- **(x)** $24x^2 - 28x + 8$

4.3 Cancelling common factors in algebraic fractions

■ Algebraic fractions can be cancelled only if there is a common factor in the numerator and the denominator.

Example 12

Simplify $\dfrac{(x-3)^2}{(x-3)}$.

Cancel by $(x-3)$: $\dfrac{(x-3)^2}{(x-3)} = x-3$ $\dfrac{(x-3)^2}{(x-3)} = \dfrac{(x-3) \times \cancel{(x-3)}}{\cancel{(x-3)}} = (x-3)$

Example 13

Simplify fully $\dfrac{6(x+2)^3(x-1)}{9(x+2)(x-1)^2}$.

Cancel by 3, by $(x+2)$ and by $(x-1)$: $\dfrac{\overset{2}{\cancel{6}}(x+2)^{\overset{2}{\cancel{3}}}\cancel{(x-1)}}{\underset{3}{\cancel{9}}\cancel{(x+2)}(x-1)^{\cancel{2}}} = \dfrac{2(x+2)^2}{3(x-1)}$

Example 14

Simplify fully $\dfrac{5x+15}{x^2+3x-4} \times \dfrac{x^2-2x+1}{x^2-9}$.

Factorize all expressions completely: $\dfrac{5x+15}{x^2+3x-4} \times \dfrac{x^2-2x+1}{x^2-9} = \dfrac{5(x+3)}{(x+4)(x-1)} \times \dfrac{(x-1)^2}{(x+3)(x-3)}$

Cancel by $(x+3)$ and by $(x-1)$: $\dfrac{5\cancel{(x+3)}}{(x+4)\cancel{(x-1)}} \times \dfrac{(x-1)^{\cancel{2}}}{\cancel{(x+3)}(x-3)} = \dfrac{5(x-1)}{(x+4)(x-3)}$

■ Dividing by an algebraic fraction is equivalent to multiplying by its reciprocal.

Example 15

Simplify fully $\dfrac{x^2-x-12}{x^2+10x+25} \div \dfrac{2x-8}{x^2-25}$.

Invert the second fraction and change ÷ to ×: $\dfrac{x^2-x-12}{x^2+10x+25} \div \dfrac{2x-8}{x^2-25} = \dfrac{x^2-x-12}{x^2+10x+25} \times \dfrac{x^2-25}{2x-8}$

Factorize all expressions completely: $\dfrac{x^2-x-12}{x^2+10x+25} \times \dfrac{x^2-25}{2x-8} = \dfrac{(x-4)(x+3)}{(x+5)^2} \times \dfrac{(x+5)(x-5)}{2(x-4)}$

Cancel by $(x-4)$ and by $(x+5)$: $\dfrac{(x-4)(x+3)}{(x+5)^2} \times \dfrac{(x+5)(x-5)}{2(x-4)} = \dfrac{(x+3)(x-5)}{2(x+5)}$

Exercise 4C   Links 20K

In questions **1–4**, simplify the expressions:

1 $\dfrac{(x+2)^2}{(x+2)}$ **2** $\dfrac{5(x-6)^3}{(x-6)}$

3 $\dfrac{(x-7)^3}{2(x-7)^2}$ **4** $\dfrac{3(x+1)}{(x+1)^2}$

In questions **5–20**, simplify the expressions fully:

5 $\dfrac{3x^2-12x}{x^2+2x}$ **6** $\dfrac{4x^2+4x}{2x^2-10x}$

7 $\dfrac{x^2+x-6}{x^2-4x+4}$ **8** $\dfrac{7x^2-35x}{x^2-x-20}$

9 $\dfrac{x^2+2x+1}{x^2-1}$ **10** $\dfrac{x^2+5x-6}{4x+24}$

11 $\dfrac{2x^2-32}{x^2-3x-4}$ **12** $\dfrac{x^2-10x+25}{x^2+x-30}$

13 $\dfrac{x^2-6x}{x+4}\times\dfrac{5x+20}{x}$ **14** $\dfrac{3x+6}{x+1}\times\dfrac{x^2-1}{4x+8}$

15 $\dfrac{x^2+6x+5}{x^2+x}\times\dfrac{6x}{2x+10}$ **16** $\dfrac{x^2-14x+49}{x^2-9x+14}\times\dfrac{x^2-2x}{x^2-49}$

17 $\dfrac{x^2-2x-24}{x^2}\div\dfrac{5x-30}{x}$ **18** $\dfrac{x^2+10x+25}{5x-10}\div\dfrac{x^2+4x-5}{2x^2-4x}$

19 $\dfrac{x^2-64}{x^2+2x+1}\div\dfrac{x^2-16x+64}{x^2-7x-8}$ **20** $\dfrac{2x^2-7x-15}{x^2+1}\div\dfrac{8x+12}{8x^2+8}$

4.4 Generating formulae

■   **You can sometimes eliminate one of the letters from a formula by substituting for it an expression from a second formula.**

Example 16

Two formulae used in the study of electricity are $P = IV$ and $V = IR$. Find a formula for P in terms of I and R.

In $P = IV$, replace V by IR.

$$P = I \times IR$$
$$P = I^2R$$

Example 17

The length of a rectangle is l and its area is A.
Find a formula for its perimeter, P, in terms of l and A.

Let b represent the breadth of the rectangle.

$$P = 2l + 2b \qquad\qquad (1)$$
$$A = lb \qquad\qquad (2)$$

Make b the subject of formula (2).

$$b = \frac{A}{l}$$

In formula (1), substitute $\dfrac{A}{l}$ for b.

$$P = 2l + \frac{2A}{l}$$

Exercise 4D

1 $P = IV$ and $V = IR$.
Find a formula for:
(a) P in terms of V and R.
(b) R in terms of V and P.

2 $s = vt$ and $v = \frac{1}{2}gt$.
Find a formula for s in terms of g and t.

3 $A = \pi r^2$ and $r = \dfrac{d}{2}$.
Find a formula for A in terms of d.

4 $a = \dfrac{v^2}{r}$ and $v = r\omega$.
Find a formula for a in terms of r and ω.

5 $y = 4t + 3$ and $x = 2t - 1$.
Find a formula for y in terms of x.

4.5 Changing the subject of a formula

- A formula (plural: formulae) can be used to describe a relationship between two sets of numbers.
- A formula must contain an equals (=) sign.
- The subject of a formula appears on its own on one side of the formula and does not appear on the other side.

Example 18

Make v the subject of the formula $E = \frac{1}{2}mv^2$.

Multiply both sides by 2: $\qquad 2E = mv^2$

Divide both sides by m: $\qquad v^2 = \dfrac{2E}{m}$

Find square root: $\qquad v = \sqrt{\dfrac{2E}{m}}$

> $v = \sqrt{\dfrac{E}{\frac{1}{2}m}}$ is also correct
>
> but it's best not to have a fraction within another fraction.

Example 19

Make r the subject of the formula $A = \pi(R^2 - r^2)$.

Expand the brackets: $\qquad A = \pi R^2 - \pi r^2$

Add πr^2 to both sides: $\qquad A + \pi r^2 = \pi R^2$

Subtract A from both sides: $\qquad \pi r^2 = \pi R^2 - A$

Divide both sides by π: $\qquad r^2 = \dfrac{\pi R^2 - A}{\pi}$

Find square root: $\qquad r = \sqrt{\dfrac{\pi R^2 - A}{\pi}}$

> Alternatively, you can start by dividing both sides by π:
>
> $\dfrac{A}{\pi} = R^2 - r^2$
>
> which leads to an answer of
>
> $r = \sqrt{R^2 - \dfrac{A}{\pi}}$

Example 20

Make m the subject of the formula $mv = (m + M)V$.

Expand the brackets: $\qquad mv = mV + MV$

Subtract mV from both sides: $\qquad mv - mV = MV$

Factorize the left-hand side: $\qquad m(v - V) = MV$

Divide both sides by $(v - V)$: $\qquad m = \dfrac{MV}{v - V}$

> The letter which you have to make the subject occurs twice.

Exercise 4E   Links 2H, 10H, 14F

Make the letter in square brackets the subject of these formulae:

1	$P = IV$	$[I]$	**2**	$A = \pi rl$	$[r]$	**3**	$y = 4x - 3$	$[x]$		
4	$t = 3n + 5$	$[n]$	**5**	$P = 2x + y$	$[y]$	**6**	$P = 2x + y$	$[x]$		
7	$v = u - gt$	$[u]$	**8**	$v = u - gt$	$[t]$	**9**	$A = \frac{1}{2}bh$	$[b]$		
10	$s = \dfrac{a + b + c}{2}$	$[a]$	**11**	$D = \dfrac{M}{V}$	$[M]$	**12**	$D = \dfrac{M}{V}$	$[V]$		
13	$I = m(v - u)$	$[v]$	**14**	$I = m(v - u)$	$[u]$	**15**	$A = \frac{1}{2}(a + b)h$	$[h]$		

16 $A = \frac{1}{2}(a+b)h$ [b]   **17** $y = \frac{1}{3}x - 2$ [x]   **18** $y = 2(x-1)$ [x]

19 $x = 3(y+2)$ [y]   **20** $H = 17 - \dfrac{A}{2}$ [A]   **21** $y = \dfrac{5-x}{2}$ [x]

22 $3x - 2y = 6$ [x]   **23** $3x - 2y = 6$ [y]   **24** $mV + MV = mv$ [V]

25 $E = mc^2$ [c]   **26** $c^2 = a^2 + b^2$ [a]   **27** $d = \dfrac{v^2}{100}$ [v]

28 $A = \pi(R^2 - r^2)$ [R]   **29** $d = L(1 + at)$ [t]   **30** $T = k(L - a)$ [a]

31 $I = \frac{4}{3}Ma^2$ [a]   **32** $E = \dfrac{Lx^2}{2a}$ [x]   **33** $y = \dfrac{x}{a} + b$ [x]

34 $uf + vf = uv$ [f]   **35** $uf + vf = uv$ [u]   **36** $y = \frac{1}{2}x^2 - 5$ [x]

37 $mv^2 = 2E + mu^2$ [m]   **38** $I = \frac{1}{3}M(a^2 + b^2)$ [a]   **39** $A - P = \dfrac{PRT}{100}$ [R]

40 $A - P = \dfrac{PRT}{100}$ [P]   **41** $\dfrac{x}{a} + \dfrac{y}{b} = 1$ [a]   **42** $F = \dfrac{GMm}{r^2}$ [r]

43 $V = \frac{1}{6}\pi D^3$ [D]   **44** $x = \dfrac{WL^3}{3EI}$ [L]   **45** $I = M\left(\dfrac{r^2}{4} + \dfrac{a^2}{3}\right)$ [r]

46 $a = \sqrt{\dfrac{I}{m}}$ [I]   **47** $v = \sqrt{2gh}$ [h]   **48** $i = \sqrt{\dfrac{e-v}{R}}$ [v]

49 $d = 5\sqrt{\dfrac{h}{2}}$ [h]   **50** $R = \sqrt{\dfrac{3M+m}{M}}$ [M]

Exercise 4F   Mixed questions

1 Expand and simplify:
(a) $(x+9)(x+2)$ (b) $(x-1)(x+7)$ (c) $(x-8)(x-2)$
(d) $(x+5)(x-3)$ (e) $(x-3)(x+3)$ (f) $(x-4)^2$
(g) $(x+8)^2$ (h) $(x-7)(2x+5)$ (i) $(4x-1)(2x-3)$
(j) $(3x-1)(3x+1)$ (k) $(3x-1)^2$ (l) $(4x+7)^2$
(m) $(2x-y)(5x+2y)$ (n) $(5x-4y)^2$ (o) $(3x+4y)(3x-4y)$

2 Factorize each of these expressions completely:
(a) $4x^2 + 7x$ (b) $27x^2 - 18$ (c) $x^2 + x$
(d) $16x^2 - 24x$ (e) $10ax^2 + 12ax$ (f) $3x^2y - 9xy$

3   Factorize each of these quadratic expressions:

(a) $x^2 + 8x + 7$ **(b)** $x^2 + x - 2$ **(c)** $x^2 - 7x + 12$

(d) $x^2 - 64$ **(e)** $x^2 - 7x - 18$ **(f)** $x^2 - 18x + 81$

(g) $3x^2 - 108$ **(h)** $3x^2 - 19x + 20$ **(i)** $16x^2 - 1$

(j) $12x^2 - 13x - 4$ **(k)** $4x^2 - 28x + 49$ **(l)** $20x^2 - 27x - 8$

4   Simplify these expressions fully:

(a) $\dfrac{(x-5)^2}{(x-5)}$ **(b)** $\dfrac{5(x-1)}{(x-1)^2}$ **(c)** $\dfrac{6(x-7)^2}{9(x-7)}$

(d) $\dfrac{12(x+2)}{8(x+2)^3}$ **(e)** $\dfrac{6x^2+12x}{4x^2-2x}$ **(f)** $\dfrac{8x^2-8x}{x^2+3x-4}$

(g) $\dfrac{x^2-6x+9}{5x^2-45}$ **(h)** $\dfrac{x^2-3x-10}{x^2-6x+5}$ **(i)** $\dfrac{x^2-9x+14}{x^2-6x-7}$

(j) $\dfrac{6x-24}{x^2-25} \times \dfrac{x+5}{3x-12}$ **(k)** $\dfrac{x^2-6x-16}{x^2-4x-32} \times \dfrac{x^2+8x+16}{x^2+2x}$

(l) $\dfrac{8x-40}{x^2+6x-7} \div \dfrac{6x-30}{x^2-1}$ **(m)** $\dfrac{x^2-20x+100}{x^2-6x-7} \div \dfrac{x^2-100}{x^2-9x+14}$

5   Make the letter in square brackets the subject of each of these formulae:

(a) $E = mgh$ $[h]$ **(b)** $V = \dfrac{D}{T}$ $[D]$ **(c)** $V = \dfrac{D}{T}$ $[T]$

(d) $V = e + IR$ $[I]$ **(e)** $S = \frac{1}{2}n(a+l)$ $[n]$ **(f)** $S = \frac{1}{2}n(a+l)$ $[l]$

6   Make y the subject of each of these formulae:

(a) $a = \dfrac{y}{b} + c$ **(b)** $a(y+b) = c$ **(c)** $a = \dfrac{by^2}{c}$

(d) $a = by^2 + c$ **(e)** $ay = by + c$ **(f)** $ay = c - by$

(g) $a(y+b) = c(y+d)$ **(h)** $a = b(y^2+c)$ **(i)** $ay^2 = by^2 + c$

(j) $ay^2 = b - cy^2$ **(k)** $a = \dfrac{by^3}{c}$ **(l)** $\dfrac{y+a}{y+b} = c$

7 $T = kx$ and $E = \frac{1}{2}Tx$.
Find a formula for E in terms of k and x.

8 $y = 5x - 2$ and $x = 2t + 1$.
Find a formula for y in terms of t.

9 $V = \pi r^2 h$ and $S = 2\pi rh$.
Find a formula for V in terms of S and r.

Summary of key points

■ $(e+f)(g+h) = e(g+h) + f(g+h)$
$\qquad\qquad = eg + eh + fg + fh$

■ In general: $(x+a)^2 = x^2 + 2ax + a^2$
$\qquad\qquad\quad (x-a)^2 = x^2 - 2ax + a^2$
$\qquad\qquad\quad (x+a)(x-a) = x^2 - a^2$ ——————— This is called the difference of two squares.

■ **Factorizing is the reverse process to expanding brackets.**

■ **A quadratic expression has the form $ax^2 + bx + c$, where $a \neq 0$.**
  ● **the coefficient of x^2 is a**
  ● **the coefficient of x is b**
  ● **the constant term is c.**

■ **Algebraic fractions can be cancelled only if there is a common factor in the numerator and the denominator.**

■ **Dividing by an algebraic fraction is equivalent to multiplying by its reciprocal.**

■ **A formula (plural: formulae) can be used to describe a relationship between two sets of numbers.**

■ **A formula must contain an equals (=) sign.**

■ **The subject of a formula appears on its own on one side of the formula and does not appear on the other side.**

5 Equations and inequalities

5.1 Simultaneous equations – graphical solutions

- Two equations in two unknowns with a common solution are called *simultaneous equations* e.g. $y = 2x - 1$ and $y = 5 - x$.
- You can solve simultaneous equations graphically.
  - Draw the two straight lines represented by the two simultaneous equations.
  - Their point of intersection represents the common solution.

Example 1

Does the point with coordinates (5, 2) lie on the line with equation $3x - 4y = 7$?

Substitute $x = 5$ and $y = 2$ into the expression $3x - 4y$:

$$3 \times 5 - 4 \times 2 = 15 - 8$$
$$= 7$$

So the point with coordinates (5, 2) does lie on the line with equation $3x - 4y = 7$.

Example 2

Solve the simultaneous equations

$$y = 2x - 1$$
$$y = 5 - x$$

Plot three points for each equation,

e.g. (1, 1), (2, 3), (3, 5) for $y = 2x - 1$
(5, 0), (0, 5), (3, 2) for $y = 5 - x$

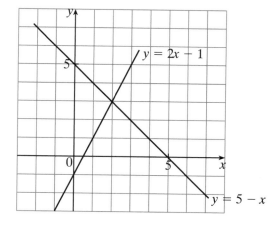

and draw the two straight lines.

The coordinates of the point of intersection of the lines gives the solution:

$$x = 2$$
$$y = 3$$

Check:

$$2 \times 2 - 1 = 3$$
$$5 - 2 = 3$$

Exercise 5A **Links 7C**

1 Write down three pairs of integer values of x and y which satisfy each of these equations:
  (a) $x + y = 7$ **(b)** $x - y = 3$ **(c)** $y = 2x - 3$
  (d) $x + 2y = 8$ **(e)** $y = 3 - x$ **(f)** $y = 5 - 2x$

2 Which of the following points lie on the line with equation $3x - 4y = 12$?
  (a) $(4, 0)$ **(b)** $(-4, 0)$ **(c)** $(0, 3)$
  (d) $(0, -3)$ **(e)** $(8, 3)$ **(f)** $(-4, 6)$

3 Which of the following points lie on the line with equation $y = 4x + 5$?
  (a) $(5, 0)$ **(b)** $(0, 5)$ **(c)** $(1, 9)$
  (d) $(9, 1)$ **(e)** $(1, -1)$ **(f)** $(-1, 1)$

4 Which of the following equations are satisfied by $x = 2$ and $y = 3$?
  (a) $x + 2y = 8$ **(b)** $y = 4x - 5$ **(c)** $5x - 2y = 4$
  (d) $4x - 3y = 1$ **(e)** $y = 7 - 2x$ **(f)** $3x - 2y = 0$

5 Which of the following equations are satisfied by $x = 5$ and $y = -2$?
  (a) $2x + 3y = 4$ **(b)** $y = x - 3$ **(c)** $x - 2y = 9$
  (d) $y = 3 - x$ **(e)** $3x - 4y = 7$ **(f)** $y = 8 - 2x$

6 Use **Diagram A** to solve the simultaneous equations

$$2x + y = 1$$
$$3x + 5y = 12$$

7 Use **Diagram B** to solve the simultaneous equations

$$2x + 3y = 12$$
$$y = x - 1$$

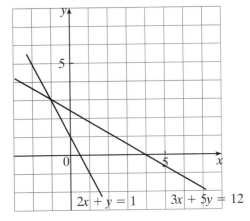

Diagram A   **Diagram B**

8 On separate diagrams, draw appropriate straight lines to solve these simultaneous equations:

(a) $x + y = 7$
$x - y = 3$

(b) $x + y = 8$
$y = x + 2$

(c) $2x + y = 8$
$x - y = 1$

(d) $y = x + 2$
$y = 2x - 1$

(e) $3x + 2y = 6$
$2x + y = 2$

(f) $2x - y = 5$
$3x - 4y = 10$

5.2 Simultaneous equations – algebraic solutions

■ You can solve simultaneous equations algebraically by eliminating one of the unknowns.
  ● If the coefficients of one of the unknowns are equal, you subtract one equation from the other.
  ● If the coefficients of one of the unknowns differ only in sign, you add the two equations.
  ● Otherwise, you multiply one or other of the equations by an appropriate number and then add or subtract.

Example 3

Solve the simultaneous equations

$$6x + 5y = 7 \qquad (1)$$
$$3x + 5y = 1 \qquad (2)$$

Label the equations with a number or a letter. The coefficients of y are equal (both 5).

$(1) - (2)$: $\qquad\qquad 3x = 6 \qquad (3)$
$(3) \div 3$: $\qquad\qquad$ so $x = 2$

Substitute in (2) to find y: $\quad 6 + 5y = 1$
$$5y = -5$$
$$y = -1$$

It does not matter which of the two original equations you substitute into but you should check that your values fit the other one as well.

The solution is $x = 2$, $y = -1$.

Exercise 5B   Links 7D

Solve these simultaneous equations:

1 $5x + y = 11$
$3x - y = 5$

2 $5x + 2y = 17$
$3x + 2y = 11$

3 $4x + 3y = 20$
$2x - 3y = 10$

4 $6x + 5y = 13$
$6x - y = 19$

5 $7x - 3y = 5$
$7x - 2y = 1$

6 $5x - 3y = 14$
$2x - 3y = 2$

7 $4x + 5y = 19$
$2x - 5y = 2$

8 $3x - 4y = -24$
$10x + 4y = -28$

9 $x + 4y = 3$
$x - 4y = -9$

10 $2x - 5y = 4$
$4x - 5y = 7$

11 $3x + 5y = 3$
$6x - 5y = 21$

12 $4x - 3y = 7$
$4x - 5y = 17$

Example 4

Solve the simultaneous equations:

$$3x + 4y = 6 \quad\quad (1)$$
$$5x - 6y = 29 \quad\quad (2)$$

(1) × 3: $\quad\quad 9x + 12y = 18 \quad\quad (3)$
(2) × 2: $\quad\quad 10x - 12y = 58 \quad\quad (4)$
(3) + (4): $\quad\quad 19x = 76$
$$x = 4$$

Substitute in (1) to find y: $\quad 12 + 4y = 6$
$$4y = -6$$
$$y = -1\tfrac{1}{2}$$

The solution is $x = 4$, $y = -1\tfrac{1}{2}$.

12 is the lowest common multiple of 4 and 6. Multiply the equations so that the coefficients of y differ only in sign.

Alternatively, you could multiply equation (1) by 5, multiply equation (2) by 3 and then subtract.

Exercise 5C | **Links 7E**

Solve these simultaneous equations:

1 $3x + 2y = 14$
$\quad 5x + 6y = 26$

2 $6x + y = 17$
$\quad 7x - 2y = 4$

3 $3x - 4y = 4$
$\quad 9x - 7y = 22$

4 $8x + 3y = 18$
$\quad 12x - 5y = 8$

5 $5x + 6y = 4$
$\quad 8x - 9y = 25$

6 $7x - 10y = 16$
$\quad 4x - 15y = 37$

7 $4x + 3y = 24$
$\quad 3x - 2y = 1$

8 $5x - 3y = 2$
$\quad 6x - 4y = 1$

9 $5x + 4y = 12$
$\quad 2x - 5y = 18$

10 $6x + 5y = 4$
$\quad 4x - 3y = 9$

11 $7x + 5y = 12$
$\quad 5x + 3y = 10$

12 $9x - 7y = 6$
$\quad 11x - 9y = 8$

5.3 Showing inequalities on a number line

■ An inequality is a statement which shows that one quantity is not equal to another quantity.

■ You can show an inequality on a number line.
An open circle ○ means a number is not included.
A filled circle ● means a number is included.

> means 'greater than'.
< means 'less than'.
⩾ means 'greater than or equal to'.
⩽ means 'less than or equal to'.

Example 5

Show the inequality $x < 2$ on a number line.

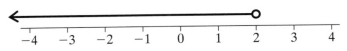

Example 6
Write down the inequality shown on this number line:

The inequality shown is $x \geqslant -1$.

Example 7
Show the inequality $-1 < x \leqslant 3$ on a number line.

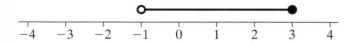

Exercise 5D	**Links 2I**

Write down the inequalities shown in questions **1–6**.

1

2
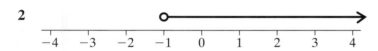

3
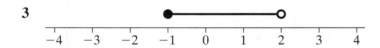

4
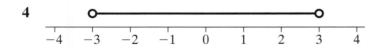

5
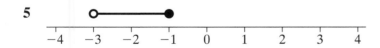

6
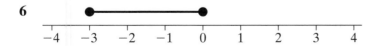

Draw number lines to show the inequalities in questions **7–15**.

7	$x < 1$	**8**	$x \geqslant 0$	**9**	$x \leqslant -1$
10	$x > -3$	**11**	$1 \leqslant x < 3$	**12**	$-2 \leqslant x \leqslant 1$
13	$-4 < x < -1$	**14**	$0 < x \leqslant 3$	**15**	$-1 \leqslant x < 2$

5.4 Solving inequalities

■ **To solve an inequality you can**
  - **add the same quantity to both sides**
  - **subtract the same quantity from both sides**
  - **multiply both sides by the same *positive* quantity**
  - **divide both sides by the same *positive* quantity**

  but you must not
  - **multiply both sides by the same *negative* quantity**
  - **divide both sides by the same *negative* quantity.**

> You solve inequalities in the same way as linear equations, except that you must not multiply or divide both sides by a *negative* number.

Example 8

Solve the inequality $3x - 10 < 7x - 1$ and show the solution on a number line.

Subtract $3x$ from both sides: $-10 < 4x - 1$

Add 1 to both sides: $-9 < 4x$ If $-9 < 4x$, then you can write $4x > -9$.

Divide both sides by 4: $x > -2\frac{1}{4}$

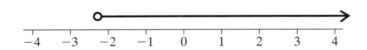

Exercise 5E   Links 2J

Solve the inequalities in questions **1–6**.

1 $5x + 3 < 18$ **2** $9 - 4x \leqslant 7$ **3** $-8x < 40$

4 $7x + 6 \leqslant 2x + 1$ **5** $2x + 7 \leqslant 1 - x$ **6** $3 - 4x > 5 - 6x$

In questions **7–15**, solve each inequality and show the solution on a number line.

7 $2x - 3 > 2$ **8** $4x - 1 < 6$ **9** $4 - 3x \leqslant 2$

10 $6x + 3 < 2x + 1$ **11** $2x + 5 < 5x - 2$ **12** $1 - 3x \geqslant 2x + 1$

13 $2x + 7 > 1 - 2x$ **14** $1 - x < 9 - 4x$ **15** $2 - 3x \leqslant 7 - x$

In questions **16–24**, solve each inequality.

16 $2x - 7 < 6$ **17** $4x + 9 \geqslant 2$ **18** $9 - 7x < 4$

19 $2 + 9x > 3x - 10$ **20** $4x + 9 \geqslant 8x + 3$ **21** $13 - 4x \leqslant 2 - 7x$

22 $5 - 8x > 2 - 3x$ **23** $1 - 2x \geqslant 12 - 7x$ **24** $1 - 8x < 3 - 5x$

5.5 Integer solutions to inequalities

Example 9
List all the integers which satisfy the inequality $-9 \leqslant 4x < 8$ and show the solutions on a number line.

Divide each term in the inequality by 4: $-2\frac{1}{4} \leqslant x < 2$

The integer solutions are $-2, -1, 0, 1$.

Integers are positive whole numbers, negative whole numbers and 0.

Example 10
Find the least integer which satisfies the inequality $2x \geqslant 4 - 3x$.

Add $3x$ to both sides: $5x \geqslant 4$

Divide both sides by 5: $x \geqslant \frac{4}{5}$

The least integer which satisfies the inequality is 1.

Exercise 5F   Links 2L

In questions **1–6**, list the integers which satisfy each of the inequalities and show them on a number line.

1 $-2 \leqslant x < 3$ **2** $-9 < 3x \leqslant 3$

3 $0 < 4x < 13$ **4** $-17 \leqslant 5x < -3$

5 $-3 \leqslant 2x \leqslant 1$ **6** $-5 < 6x \leqslant 18$

In questions **7–12**, list the integers which satisfy each of the inequalities.

7 $13 < 2x < 20$ **8** $-20 \leqslant 3x < -13$

9 $-3 < 4x \leqslant 8$ **10** $-25 \leqslant 5x \leqslant -7$

11 $-28 < 8x < 16$ **12** $-15 \leqslant 10x < 35$

13 Find the greatest integer which satisfies the inequality $5x + 2 \leqslant 4$.

14 Find the least integer which satisfies the inequality $6x - 1 \geqslant 2x - 7$.

15 Find the greatest integer which satisfies the inequality $2x - 3 < 7 - 3x$.

5.6 Regions

■ **You can use regions on a graph to represent inequalities.**

Example 11

Draw a diagram to represent the inequality $y \leqslant 4$.

The **unshaded** region represents the inequality
$y \leqslant 4$.
Every point below the line $y = 4$ satisfies this
inequality.
Because the inequality is 'less than **or equal to**',
every point **on** the line $y = 4$ also satisfies the
inequality and so it is drawn as a solid line to
show that it is included in the region.

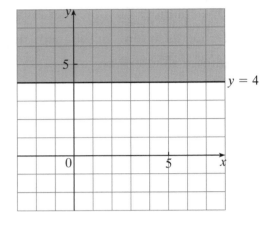

Example 12

Draw a diagram to represent the inequality
$2x + 5y < 10$.

The unshaded region represents the inequality
$2x + 5y < 10$.
The line $2x + 5y = 10$ is dotted because points on
the line do not satisfy the inequality and so it is
in the unwanted region. To find which side of the
line $2x + 5y = 10$ satisfies the inequality,
substitute the x- and y-coordinates of a point,
often the origin, into the inequality.
In this case, letting $x = 0$ and $y = 0$ does satisfy
the inequality and so the origin does lie in the
required region.

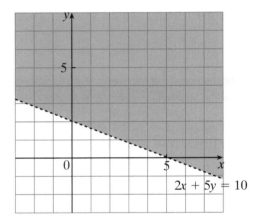

Example 13

Draw a diagram to represent the inequality $y \geqslant \frac{1}{2}x$.

The unshaded region represents the inequality $y \geqslant \frac{1}{2}x$.
The line $y = \frac{1}{2}x$ is solid, because points on the
line do satisfy the inequality.
As the line passes through the origin, test with a
different point, for example $(2, 0)$. Letting $x = 2$
and $y = 0$ does not satisfy the inequality and so
$(2, 0)$ lies in the unwanted region.

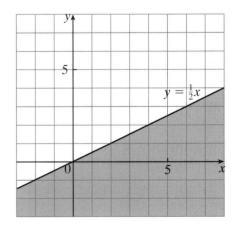

Example 14

Draw a diagram to show the region which satisfies
all three of the inequalities

$$x \geqslant 1, \ y > 2, \ x + y \leqslant 7$$

The required region is **unshaded**.

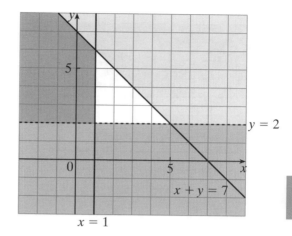

Example 15

Draw a diagram to show the region
which satisfies all three of the
inequalities

$$x + 2y > 8, \ y < 6, \ y \geqslant x - 1$$

Mark with a dot on your graph every
point with integer coordinates which
satisfies all three inequalities.

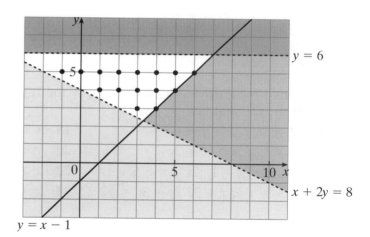

Exercise 5G   Links 7G

In questions **1–12**, draw diagrams to show the regions which satisfy
the inequalities. Shade the **unwanted** regions.

1 $x \leqslant 5$	**2** $y > 4$	**3** $x + y > 4$
4 $-2 \leqslant x < 3$	**5** $y < 3x$	**6** $2x + y > 8$
7 $y < x + 1$	**8** $x - y \leqslant 3$	**9** $y \geqslant 2x + 3$
10 $3x + 5y \leqslant 15$	**11** $y < 6 - 2x$	**12** $2x - 3y > 6$

In questions **13–16**, find inequalities which describe the unshaded regions.

13

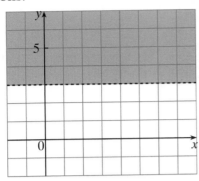

14

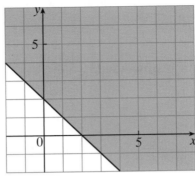

15

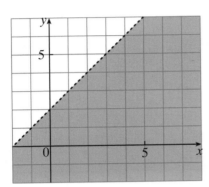

16

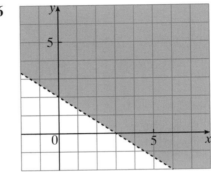

In questions **17–24**, draw diagrams to show the regions which satisfy **all** the inequalities.

17 $x > 2$, $y \geqslant 1$, $x + y < 6$

18 $x \geqslant 0$, $y < 4$, $y \geqslant x$

19 $y \leqslant x + 3$, $y \geqslant 0$, $x + 2y < 6$

20 $y < 2x$, $x + y \geqslant 2$, $x < 2$

21 $x \geqslant 0$, $y \geqslant 2x - 1$, $2x + y < 6$

22 $x \geqslant 1$, $x - y < 2$, $y \leqslant \frac{1}{2}x + 1$

23 $x + y > 3$, $y < x + 3$, $2x + 3y \leqslant 12$

24 $x + y \geqslant 2$, $y > x - 2$, $y < 8 - 2x$, $y \leqslant 3x + 2$

In questions **25–30**, draw a diagram to show the regions which satisfy all the inequalities. Mark with a dot on each graph every point with integer coordinates which satisfies all the inequalities.

25 $x \geqslant 3$, $y > 2$, $x + y \leqslant 7$

26 $x < 5$, $y \geqslant 2$, $y \leqslant x$

27 $x \leqslant 3$, $y < x + 2$, $2x + y \geqslant 4$

28 $y < 2x + 3$, $x + y \geqslant 3$, $2x + y < 6$

29 $y \geqslant 0$, $x - y \leqslant 4$, $y < \frac{1}{2}x$, $2x + y > 4$

30 $x \geqslant 0$, $x - y \leqslant 3$, $x + y > 5$, $3x + 4y < 24$

5.7 Solving quadratic equations by factorizing

- Equations of the form $ax^2 + bx + c = 0$, where $a \neq 0$, are called *quadratic* equations.

- The quadratic equation $ax^2 + bx + c = 0$, where $a \neq 0$, has two solutions (or roots), which may be equal.

- If $xy = 0$, then either $x = 0$ or $y = 0$.

Example 16

Solve the equation $x^2 + 4x - 5 = 0$.

Factorize: $(x + 5)(x - 1) = 0$
Either $x + 5 = 0$ or $x - 1 = 0$

The two solutions are $x = -5$, $x = 1$.

> You must have zero on one side of a quadratic equation before you try to factorize the other side.

Example 17

Solve the equation $x^2 + 3x = 0$.

Factorize: $x(x + 3) = 0$
Either $x = 0$ or $x + 3 = 0$

The two solutions are $x = 0$, $x = -3$.

> Don't divide both sides of the equation by x. If you do, you will lose the $x = 0$ solution.

Example 18

Solve the equation $x^2 - 64 = 0$.

Factorize: $(x + 8)(x - 8) = 0$
Either $x + 8 = 0$ or $x - 8 = 0$

The two solutions are $x = -8$, $x = 8$.

> In general,
> $$x^2 - a^2 = (x + a)(x - a)$$
> This is called the difference between two squares.

Example 19

Solve the equation $10x^2 + 9x - 15 = 2x - 3$.

Rearrange in the form
$ax^2 + bx + c = 0$: $10x^2 + 7x - 12 = 0$
Factorize: $(2x + 3)(5x - 4) = 0$
Either $2x + 3 = 0$ or $5x - 4 = 0$

The two solutions are $x = -1\frac{1}{2}$, $x = \frac{4}{5}$.

Exercise 5H   Links 21A

1   Solve these equations:
    (a) $(x - 4)(x - 5) = 0$ **(b)** $(x + 3)(x - 8) = 0$
    (c) $(x + 8)(x + 1) = 0$ **(d)** $x(x - 6) = 0$
    (e) $(x - 7)(x + 2) = 0$ **(f)** $(x + 9)(x - 9) = 0$
    (g) $x(x + 2) = 0$ **(h)** $3(x + 6)(x - 4) = 0$
    (i) $(2x - 1)(3x - 2) = 0$ **(j)** $(2x - 5)(5x + 2) = 0$

2   Solve these equations:
    (a) $x^2 - 5x + 6 = 0$ **(b)** $x^2 + 6x - 7 = 0$
    (c) $x^2 + 10x + 16 = 0$ **(d)** $x^2 - 5x = 0$
    (e) $x^2 - 4 = 0$ **(f)** $x^2 - 8x + 16 = 0$
    (g) $x^2 + 9x = 0$ **(h)** $x^2 - x - 20 = 0$
    (i) $x^2 - 100 = 0$ **(j)** $x^2 + 12x + 36 = 0$

3 Solve these equations:
  (a) $5x^2 - 15x + 10 = 0$ **(b)** $2x^2 - 4x - 48 = 0$
  (c) $7x^2 - 7 = 0$ **(d)** $4x^2 + 24x = 0$
  (e) $3x^2 + 21x + 36 = 0$ **(f)** $9x^2 - 36x + 36 = 0$
  (g) $6x^2 - 42x = 0$ **(h)** $4x^2 + 40x + 100 = 0$
  (i) $2x^2 - 50 = 0$ **(j)** $5x^2 - 35x - 90 = 0$

4 Solve these equations:
  (a) $5x^2 - 7x - 6 = 0$ **(b)** $2x^2 - x - 15 = 0$
  (c) $6x^2 - 13x + 5 = 0$ **(d)** $10x^2 - x - 21 = 0$
  (e) $4x^2 - 25 = 0$ **(f)** $9x^2 - 12x + 4 = 0$
  (g) $20x^2 - 23x + 6 = 0$ **(h)** $4x^2 + 28x + 49 = 0$
  (i) $9x^2 - 4 = 0$ **(j)** $8x^2 + 22x - 21 = 0$

5 Solve these equations:
  (a) $2x^2 = x$ **(b)** $3x^2 = 48$
  (c) $x^2 + x = 42$ **(d)** $x^2 + 4x - 5 = x + 13$
  (e) $(x + 4)(x + 1) = x$ **(f)** $x^2 = 15 - 2x$
  (g) $(x - 2)(x - 6) = 2x - 13$ **(h)** $12x^2 = 13x - 1$
  (i) $(2x - 3)(3x - 5) = 5$ **(j)** $(5x - 2)^2 = 20(1 - x)$

5.8 Solving quadratic equations by completing the square

Teaching reference:
(*pp 382–384, section 21.2*)

■ To make the expression $x^2 + 2ax$ a perfect square, you add a^2. $(x + a)^2 = x^2 + 2ax + a^2$

■ Completing the square: $x^2 + bx = \left(x + \dfrac{b}{2}\right)^2 - \left(\dfrac{b}{2}\right)^2.$

Example 20
Write each of the following in the form $(x + b)^2 + q$: b is $\frac{1}{2}$ the coefficient of x.
(a) $x^2 + 10x$ (b) $x^2 - 8x + 21$

(a) $x^2 + 10x = (x + 5)^2 - 25$ $(x + 5)^2 = x^2 + 10x + 25$ so you subtract 25.
(b) $x^2 - 8x + 21 = (x - 4)^2 + 5$ $(x - 4)^2 = x^2 - 8x + 16$ so you add 5.

Example 21
Write $3x^2 + 24x + 55$ in the form $a(x + p)^2 + q$.

$$3x^2 + 24x + 55 = 3(x^2 + 8x) + 55$$
$$= 3[(x + 4)^2 - 16] + 55$$
$$= 3(x + 4)^2 - 48 + 55$$
$$= 3(x + 4)^2 + 7$$

Exercise 5I   Links 21B

1 Write the following in the form $(x+p)^2+q$:
   (a) x^2+6x **(b)** x^2-2x **(c)** x^2+3x
   (d) $x^2+8x+13$ **(e)** x^2-4x+7 **(f)** $x^2+12x+30$
   (g) $x^2-10x+35$ **(h)** $x^2+20x+80$ **(i)** x^2-5x+4

2 Write the following in the form $a(x+p)^2+q$:
   (a) $2x^2+4x$ **(b)** $3x^2-30x$ **(c)** $5x^2+30x$
   (d) $4x^2-16x+21$ **(e)** $6x^2+36x+47$ **(f)** $7x^2-14x+10$
   (g) $3x^2-3x+1$ **(h)** $5x^2+15x+9$ **(i)** $6x^2-30x+37$

Example 22

Solve the equation $x^2-6x+4=0$.
Give your answers (a) in surd form, (b) correct to 2 d.p.

> The square roots of all whole numbers except square numbers are surds e.g. $\sqrt{2}$, $\sqrt{3}$, $\sqrt{5}$.

(a) Subtract 4 to get constant term on RHS: $x^2-6x=-4$
    Complete the square for x^2-6x: $(x-3)^2-9=-4$
    Add 9 to both sides: $(x-3)^2=5$
    Square root both sides: $x-3=\pm\sqrt{5}$
    Add 3 to both sides: $x=3\pm\sqrt{5}$

In surd form, the solutions are $x=3+\sqrt{5}$ or $x=3-\sqrt{5}$.
(b) Correct to 2 d.p., the solutions are $x=5.24$ or $x=0.76$.

Exercise 5J   Links 21C

1 Solve these equations by completing the square.
Leave your answers in surd form.
   (a) $x^2-4x-1=0$ **(b)** $x^2+8x+5=0$
   (c) $x^2-10x+8=0$ **(d)** $x^2+6x-1=0$
   (e) $2x^2+12x+5=0$ **(f)** $3x^2-12x-7=0$
   (g) $x^2-5x+3=0$ **(h)** $x^2+9x-4=0$

2 Solve these equations by completing the square.
Give your answers correct to 2 d.p.
   (a) $x^2+2x-4=0$ **(b)** $x^2-8x+9=0$
   (c) $x^2-6x+3=0$ **(d)** $x^2+4x-6=0$
   (e) $2x^2+4x-1=0$ **(f)** $5x^2-20x+2=0$
   (g) $x^2-3x+1=0$ **(h)** $x^2+7x-2=0$

5.9 Solving quadratic equations using the formula

Teaching reference:
(*pp 385–388, section 21.3*)

- The roots of the quadratic equation $ax^2 + bx + c = 0$, where $a \neq 0$, are given by the formula

$$x = \frac{-b \pm \sqrt{b^2 - 4ac}}{2a}$$

This formula will be on examination formulae sheets but you must know how to use it.

- The sum of the roots of $ax^2 + bx + c = 0$ is $\dfrac{-b}{a}$.

- The product of the roots of $ax^2 + bx + c = 0$ is $\dfrac{c}{a}$.

These two results are useful for checking your solutions to quadratic equations.

- If $\sqrt{b^2 - 4ac}$ is an integer, then $ax^2 + bx + c$ can be factorized.

Example 23
Solve the equation $5x^2 - 9x + 2 = 0$.
Give your answers (a) in surd form, (b) correct to 2 d.p.

(a) $\quad x = \dfrac{9 \pm \sqrt{(-9)^2 - 4 \times 5 \times 2}}{2 \times 5}$

$x = \dfrac{9 \pm \sqrt{81 - 40}}{10}$

$x = \dfrac{9 \pm \sqrt{41}}{10}$

In surd form, the solutions are $x = \dfrac{9 + \sqrt{41}}{10}$ or $x = \dfrac{9 - \sqrt{41}}{10}$.

(b) Correct to 2 d.p., the solutions are $x = 1.54$ or $x = 0.26$.

Exercise 5K   Links 21D

1   Solve these equations using the formula.
    Leave your answers in surd form.

   (a) $x^2 - 3x + 1 = 0$ (b) $x^2 + 5x + 3 = 0$
   (c) $x^2 - 6x - 2 = 0$ (d) $x^2 + 7x - 5 = 0$
   (e) $2x^2 + 6x - 3 = 0$ (f) $3x^2 - 9x + 2 = 0$
   (g) $4x^2 + 7x + 2 = 0$ (h) $5x^2 - 4x - 3 = 0$
   (i) $3x^2 + 8x + 2 = 0$ (j) $4x^2 - 5x - 3 = 0$

In parts (a)–(d), $a = 1$.

2 Solve these equations using the formula.
Give your answers correct to 2 d.p.
(a) $x^2 + 4x - 2 = 0$ (b) $x^2 - x - 9 = 0$
(c) $x^2 + 8x + 5 = 0$ (d) $x^2 - 7x + 4 = 0$
(e) $2x^2 - 5x - 1 = 0$ (f) $3x^2 + 7x + 3 = 0$
(g) $4x^2 - 10x + 5 = 0$ (h) $5x^2 + 3x - 4 = 0$
(i) $2x^2 + x - 7 = 0$ (j) $5x^2 - 9x + 2 = 0$

3 Solve these equations using the formula.
Give your answers correct to 2 d.p.
(a) $x^2 + 7x - 2 = 2x + 1$ (b) $(x + 2)^2 = 7 - x$
(c) $(x + 3)(x - 3) = 3(x - 1)$ (d) $(x - 1)^2 + 5 = 6x$
(e) $2x(x + 3) = 5$ (f) $(2x + 1)(x + 4) = 3x + 1$
(g) $(2x - 1)^2 = 2(4x - 1)$ (h) $(3x - 2)(2x + 5) = 6x - 7$
(i) $3x^2 - 4x + 1 = x^2 + 2x - 1$ (j) $(2x - 3)^2 - (x - 2)^2 = 2$

Exercise 5L   Mixed questions

1 On separate diagrams, draw appropriate straight lines to solve
these simultaneous equations:
(a) $x + y = 6$ (b) $2x + y = 10$ (c) $3x + 2y = 18$
    $x - y = 2$ $y = x + 1$ $y = 2x + 2$

2 Solve these simultaneous equations:
(a) $4x + 3y = 19$ (b) $7x + 2y = 17$ (c) $5x + 6y = 14$
    $5x - 3y = 17$ $7x - 5y = 31$ $7x + 6y = 16$

3 Solve these simultaneous equations:
(a) $3x + 5y = 3$ (b) $3x + 5y = 27$ (c) $8x - 3y = 13$
    $9x + 7y = 21$ $5x - 3y = 11$ $6x - 5y = 18$

4 Draw number lines to show these inequalities:
(a) $x \leqslant 3$ (b) $x > -2$ (c) $-3 \leqslant x < 0$

5 Solve each inequality and show the solution on a number line:
(a) $2x + 7 \leqslant 4$ (b) $7x - 4 > 3x + 5$ (c) $5x + 9 \geqslant 9 - 3x$

6 Solve these inequalities:
(a) $5x + 8 < 4$ (b) $7x - 3 \geqslant 3x + 11$ (c) $4x + 1 > 5 - 2x$

7 List the integers which satisfy these inequalities and show
them on a number line:
(a) $-7 \leqslant 2x < 2$ (b) $0 \leqslant 3x \leqslant 8$ (c) $-8 < 5x < 4$

8 Draw diagrams to show the regions which satisfy these
inequalities. Shade the **unwanted** regions.
(a) $x > 3$ (b) $x + y > -1$ (c) $y \leqslant x + 4$

9 **(a)** Draw a diagram to show the regions which satisfy all these inequalities:

$$y < x + 3, \quad x + y \geqslant 3, \quad 2x + y \leqslant 6$$

(b) Mark with a dot on the graph every point with integer coordinates which satisfies all the inequalities.

10 Solve these quadratic equations by factorizing:
(a) $x^2 + 2x - 35 = 0$ **(b)** $x^2 - 10x = 0$
(c) $x^2 - 81 = 0$ **(d)** $6x^2 + 17x - 45 = 0$

11 Solve these quadratic equations by completing the square:
(a) $x^2 + 10x - 7 = 0$ **(b)** $x^2 - 7x + 4 = 0$

12 Solve these quadratic equations using the formula:
(a) $x^2 + 2x - 7 = 0$ **(b)** $2x^2 + 8x + 5 = 0$
(c) $3x^2 - x - 6 = 0$ **(d)** $4x^2 + 9x + 3 = 0$

Summary of key points

■ Two equations in two unknowns with a common solution are called *simultaneous equations*.

■ You can solve simultaneous equations graphically.
- Draw the two straight lines represented by the two simultaneous equations.
- Their point of intersection represents the common solution.

■ You can solve simultaneous equations algebraically by eliminating one of the unknowns.
- If the coefficients of one of the unknowns are equal, you subtract one equation from the other.
- If the coefficients of one of the unknowns differ only in sign, you add the two equations.
- Otherwise, you multiply one or other of the equations by an appropriate number and then add or subtract.

■ An inequality is a statement which shows that one quantity is not equal to another quantity.

> $>$ means 'greater than'.
> $<$ means 'less than'.
> $\geqslant$ means 'greater than or equal to'.
> $\leqslant$ means 'less than or equal to'.

■ You can show an inequality on a number line.
An open circle ○ means a number is not included.
A filled circle ● means a number is included.

■ To solve an inequality you can
- add the same quantity to both sides
- subtract the same quantity from both sides
- multiply both sides by the same *positive* quantity
- divide both sides by the same *positive* quantity
but you must not
- multiply both sides by the same *negative* quantity
- divide both sides by the same *negative* quantity.

> You solve inequalities in the same way as linear equations, except that you must not multiply or divide both sides by a *negative* number.

- You can use regions on a graph to represent inequalities.

- Equations of the form $ax^2 + bx + c = 0$, where $a \neq 0$, are called *quadratic* equations.

- The quadratic equation $ax^2 + bx + c = 0$, where $a \neq 0$, has two solutions (or roots), which may be equal.

- If $xy = 0$, then either $x = 0$ or $y = 0$.

- You can solve some quadratic equations by factorizing one side if you have zero on the other side.

- $x^2 - a^2 = (x + a)(x - a)$. This is called the difference of two squares.

- To make the expression $x^2 + 2ax$ a perfect square, you add a^2.

- Completing the square: $x^2 + bx = \left(x + \dfrac{b}{2}\right)^2 - \left(\dfrac{b}{2}\right)^2$.

- The roots of the quadratic equation $ax^2 + bx + c = 0$, where $a \neq 0$, are given by the formula

$$x = \frac{-b \pm \sqrt{b^2 - 4ac}}{2a}$$

- The sum of the roots of $ax^2 + bx + c = 0$ is $\dfrac{-b}{a}$.

- The product of the roots of $ax^2 + bx + c = 0$ is $\dfrac{c}{a}$.

- If $\sqrt{b^2 - 4ac}$ is an integer, then $ax^2 + bx + c$ can be factorized.

6 Area and volume

6.1 Area of a triangle

- **Area of a triangle = $\frac{1}{2}ab \sin C$**

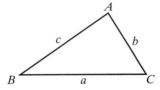

> Notice that the angle is between the sides, and side a is opposite angle A.

The formula works for acute and obtuse angled triangles.

Example 1

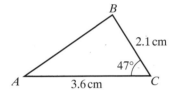

$a = 2.1\,\text{cm}$
$b = 3.6\,\text{cm}$
$C = 47°$

Area $= \frac{1}{2} \times 2.1 \times 3.6 \times \sin 47° = 2.76\,\text{cm}^2$

(An answer to three significant figures is the expected accuracy.)

For angles between 90° and 180°

- $\sin x = \sin (180 - x)$
- $\cos x = -\cos (180 - x)$

This means $\sin 127 = \sin (180 - 127) = \sin 53$
and $\cos 127 = -\cos (180 - 127) = -\cos 53$.

Example 2

The area of $\triangle PQR$ is $28.6\,\text{cm}^2$.
Sides PQ and PR are $10.9\,\text{cm}$ and $8.5\,\text{cm}$ respectively.
Find angle P.

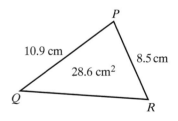

Area $= \frac{1}{2}PQ \cdot PR \sin P$

$28.6 = \frac{1}{2} \times 10.9 \times 8.5 \sin P$

$\sin P = \dfrac{28.6 \times 2}{10.9 \times 8.5} = 0.6174$ (4 d.p.)

angle $P = 38.1°$ (3 s.f.)

This is the acute angle.
However, angle $P = 141.9°$ is also a correct solution because
$\sin x = \sin (180 - x)$.

Exercise 6A   **Links 22A**

In questions **1–8** work out the area of the shape.

1
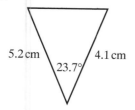
5.2 cm 4.1 cm 23.7°

2
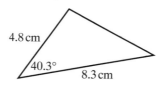
4.8 cm 40.3° 8.3 cm

3

5.2 cm 123° 7.3 cm

4
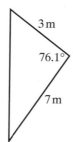
3 m 76.1° 7 m

5
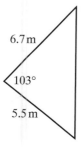
6.7 m 103° 5.5 m

6
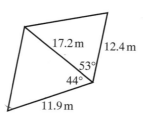
17.2 m 12.4 m 53° 44° 11.9 m

7
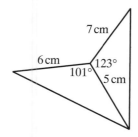
7 cm 6 cm 123° 101° 5 cm

8
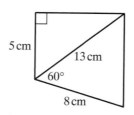
5 cm 13 cm 60° 8 cm

9 The area of $\triangle ABC$ is known to be 70 cm^2.
Find angle A (there are two possible answers).

15.1 cm 18.2 cm A B C

10 The area of $\triangle PQR$ is known to be $82.6\,\text{cm}^2$.
Angle P is obtuse. Find angle P.

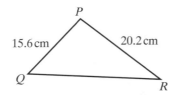

6.2 Arcs and sectors

Teaching reference:
(*pp 334–340, section 19.1*)
pp 384–390, section 19.1

■ **Length of an arc** $= \dfrac{\theta}{360} \times 2\pi r$

■ **Area of a sector** $= \dfrac{\theta}{360} \times \pi r^2$

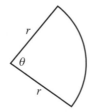

This is $\dfrac{\theta}{360}$ of a full circle.

Example 3

Calculate (a) the area and (b) the perimeter of the sector shown:

(a) $\text{Area} = \dfrac{116}{360} \times \pi \times 15^2$

$= 72.5\pi = 228\,\text{cm}^2$

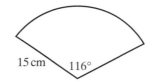

(b) $\text{Arc length} = \dfrac{116}{360} \times 2\pi \times 15$

$= \dfrac{3480\pi}{360} = 30.4\,\text{cm}$ (3 s.f.)

$\text{Perimeter} = 15 + 15 + 30.4 = 60.4\,\text{cm}$ (3 s.f.)

Exercise 6B   Links 19A, 19B

In questions **1** and **2** calculate the length of the arcs, the perimeters and the areas of the sectors shown. In question **1**, give your answers in terms of π.

1 **(a)**

24° 6 cm

(b)

40° 18 cm

(c)

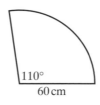

110°
60 cm

(d)

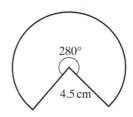

280°
4.5 cm

2   Give your answers to 1 decimal place.

(a)   23° 15 cm

(b) 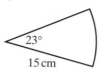 57° 6.3 cm

(c) 5.9 cm 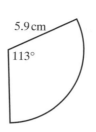 113°

(d) 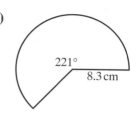 221° 8.3 cm

3   Work out the marked angles:

(a) 9 cm 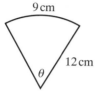 12 cm θ

(b) 12 cm 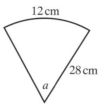 28 cm a

(c) 15 cm 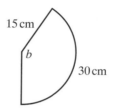 b 30 cm

(d) 32 cm 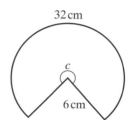 c 6 cm

6.3 Surface areas

- **Surface area of a cylinder $= 2\pi rh + 2\pi r^2$**

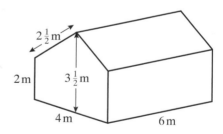 πr^2 $2\pi rh$

- **Surface area of a cone $= \pi rl + \pi r^2$**

slant height l πrl πr^2

- **Surface area of a sphere $= 4\pi r^2$**

Example 4

Work out the total surface area (not including the floor) of the shed shown. The height of the shed is $3\frac{1}{2}$ m.

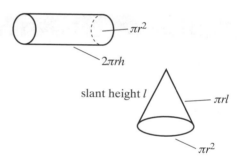 $2\frac{1}{2}$ m   2 m $3\frac{1}{2}$ m   4 m   6 m

The total surface area is comprised of (i) 2 end sections
(ii) the roof
(iii) the 2 sides.

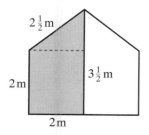 $2\frac{1}{2}$ m   2 m $3\frac{1}{2}$ m   2 m

Shaded area $= \frac{1}{2}(2 + 3\frac{1}{2}) \times 2 = 5\frac{1}{2}$ m^2 (area of trapezium)

Area of one end $= 2 \times 5\frac{1}{2} = 11$ m^2

Area of roof $= (2\frac{1}{2} + 2\frac{1}{2}) \times 6 = 30$ m^2

Area of sides $= (2 \times 6) \times 2 = 24$ m^2

Total area (not including the floor) $= 22 + 30 + 24 = 76$ m^2

Example 5

A cone has base circumference 36 cm and height 10 cm.
Work out its total surface area.

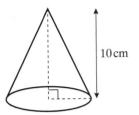

10 cm

To find the base radius:
$$2\pi r = 36$$
$$r = 5.73 \text{ cm} \quad (2 \text{ d.p.})$$

To find the slant height:
$$l^2 = 10^2 + 5.73^2 \qquad \text{(By Pythagoras)}$$
$$l = 11.525 \text{ cm} \quad (3 \text{ d.p.})$$

Surface area $= \pi r^2 + \pi r l$
$$= \pi(5.73)^2 + \pi \times 5.73 \times 11.525$$
$$= 98.9\pi \quad (1 \text{ d.p.})$$
$$= 310.6 \text{ cm}^2 \quad (1 \text{ d.p.})$$

Exercise 6C   **Links 19E, 19G**

In these questions work out the total surface area.

1

8 m   15 m

10 m

17 m

2

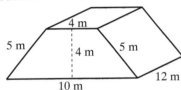

4 m

5 m   4 m   5 m

10 m   12 m

3

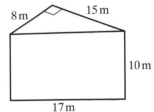

15 m

30 m

20 m

The shape is a prism with a regular hexagon as its cross-section.

4

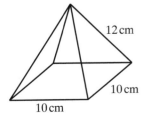

12 cm

10 cm

10 cm

5

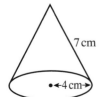

7 cm

4 cm

6

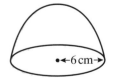

6 cm

7

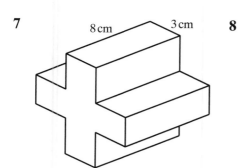

8 cm   3 cm

The length is 8 cm.
All other edges are 3 cm.

8

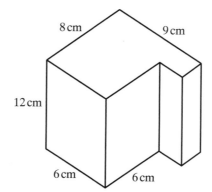

8 cm   9 cm

12 cm

6 cm   6 cm

9

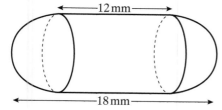

←——12 mm——→

←———18 mm———→

10

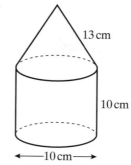

13 cm

10 cm

←—10 cm—→

6.4 Problems involving volumes of prisms and cylinders

Teaching reference:
pp 391–394, section 19.2

- Volume of a cylinder $= \pi r^2 h$
- Volume of a prism = **area of base × height**
  = area of cross-section × vertical height

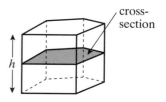

cross-section

h

Example 6

A water trough is 220 cm long. Its cross-section is a trapezium 20 cm across at the base and 26 cm across at the top. It is 10 cm deep. How many litres of water does it hold?

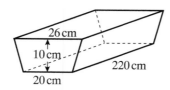

26 cm

10 cm

20 cm

220 cm

Cross-section $= \frac{1}{2}(20 + 26) \times 10 = 230 \text{ cm}^2$

Volume $= 230 \times 220 = 50\,600 \text{ cm}^3$

$\qquad\qquad\quad = 50.6 \text{ litres}$

Example 7

Water flows down a copper pipe at 24 m/s. The pipe has a diameter of 18 mm. How much water does it deliver per minute?

It is best to work in cm:
$$24\,\text{m} = 2400\,\text{cm}$$
$$18\,\text{mm} = 1.8\,\text{cm}$$

Pipe radius $= 0.9$ cm.
In 1 second 24 metres of pipe is emptied.
This volume is $\pi r^2 h = \pi \times (0.9)^2 \times 2400 = 1944\pi\,\text{cm}^3$
$$= 6107\,\text{cm}^3 \quad (4\ \text{s.f.})$$
$$= 6.107\ \text{litres}$$

So, in one minute the water delivered will be
$$6.107 \times 60 = 366\ \text{litres (to 3 s.f.)}$$

Exercise 6D

1   A wind tunnel is in the shape of a long cylinder. The diameter is 3 metres and the length is 8 metres.
    (a) The curved surface is to be soundproofed.
         What area is this?
    (b) What is the volume of the tunnel?
    (c) When the wind speed created is 40 m/s, how many cubic metres are pumped through the tunnel per second?

2   Water flows into an empty cylinder at 50 litres per second. The cylinder is 6 metres high and has radius 1.5 metres. How long does it take to fill?

3   The cross-section of a girder is shown. It is 5 metres long. Find its volume.

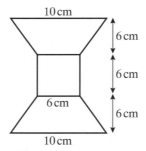

4   A hexagonal nut is made from a regular hexagon of side 15 mm with a cylindrical hole, radius 4 mm. The nut is 1.2 cm thick. Work out the volume of the nut.

5   The diagram shows the cross-section of a concrete channel:

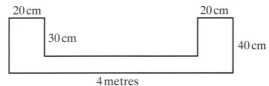

How many cubic metres of concrete are required to make 1 km of channel?

6 A country mints a coin which is circular with a circular hole in the middle. The coins are 1 mm thick. The internal radius is 5 mm and the external diameter is 25 mm. How many coins can be minted from a cubic metre of metal?

6.5 Volumes of pyramids, cones and spheres

Teaching reference: pp 394–398, section 19.2

- Volume of a pyramid $= \frac{1}{3} \times$ base area $\times$ vertical height
- Volume of a cone $= \frac{1}{3} \times$ base area $\times$ vertical height

  $= \frac{1}{3}\pi r^2 h$
- Volume of a sphere $= \frac{4}{3}\pi r^3$

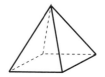

Example 8

Steel ball bearings are cast from 3000 cm³ of molten metal.
Each ball bearing has a diameter of 4 mm.
How many can be made?

As the volume is in cm³ it is easiest to work in cm.
4 mm = 0.4 cm and the radius is 0.2 cm.

Volume of 1 ball bearing $= \frac{4}{3}\pi r^3 = \frac{4}{3}\pi \times (0.2)^3$

$= 0.033\,5103\,\text{cm}^3$

Do *not* round at this stage as this loses accuracy.

Number of ball bearings cast $= 3000 \div 0.033\,5103 = 89\,524$

(In this case it must be a whole number rounded down.)
A sensible answer would be 89 500 (or 89 000).

Exercise 6E

In questions **1–5**, work out the volume.

1
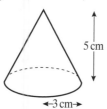
5 cm
←3 cm→

2
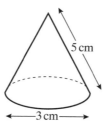
5 cm
←3 cm→

3
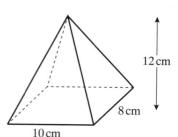
12 cm
8 cm
10 cm

4

A sphere,
diameter 18 cm

5
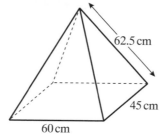
62.5 cm
45 cm
60 cm

6 A grain silo is in the shape of an inverted cone surmounted by a cylinder as shown:

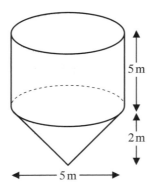

5 m

2 m

5 m

(a) How much grain does it hold when full?

(b) If 1 litre of paint covers about 15 m^2, how much paint would be required to paint the outside of the silo?

6.6 Speed and density

■ **Average speed** = $\dfrac{\textbf{total distance}}{\textbf{total time}}$

■ **Density** = $\dfrac{\textbf{mass}}{\textbf{volume}}$

In questions on speed and density it is always best to sort out the units you are going to use before commencing any calculation. Also, do not round values until the final answer.

Example 9

A solid concrete decorative cone, radius 8 cm and height 32 cm, has a mass of 6 kg. What is the density of the concrete?

$$\text{Volume of cone} = \tfrac{1}{3}\pi r^2 h = \tfrac{1}{3}\pi \times 8^2 \times 32 = 2144.66 \text{ cm}^3$$

$$\text{Density} = \frac{6000}{2144.66} = 2.8 \text{ g/cm}^3 \quad (1 \text{ d.p.})$$

Exercise 6F

1 The express train from London to Preston does the 209 miles in 2 hours 35 minutes. Work out the average speed.

2 The first part of a car journey is 120 km in 2 hours 5 minutes. After a 15 minute break the remaining 200 km is completed in a further 3 hours 10 minutes. Work out the average speed for the entire journey.

3   Jane travels for 17 minutes at an average speed of 60 kph followed by 25 minutes at an average speed of 27 kph. Work out the total distance travelled and the overall average speed.

4   The book-end shown is made from wood with a density of 0.8 g/cm³. Work out the mass of a pair of these book-ends.

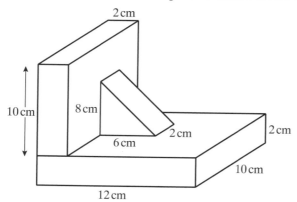

5   15 steel ball bearings displace 13.6 cm³ of water. They have a mass of 222 g. Work out the density of the steel.

6   The density of glass used to make marbles is 2.3 g/cm³. Find the mass of 12 marbles, each of which has a radius of 7 mm.

Summary of key points

- Area of a triangle $= \frac{1}{2}ab\sin C$

- Length of an arc $= \dfrac{\theta}{360} \times 2\pi r$

- Area of a sector $= \dfrac{\theta}{360} \times \pi r^2$

- Surface area of a cylinder $= 2\pi rh + 2\pi r^2$
- Surface area of a cone $= \pi rl + \pi r^2$
- Surface area of a sphere $= 4\pi r^2$
- Volume of a cylinder $= \pi r^2 h$
- Volume of a prism = area of base × height
  $\qquad\qquad$ = area of cross-section × vertical height
- Volume of a pyramid $= \frac{1}{3} \times$ base area × vertical height
- Volume of a cone $= \frac{1}{3} \times$ base area × vertical height
  $\qquad\qquad = \frac{1}{3}\pi r^2 h$
- Volume of a sphere $= \frac{4}{3}\pi r^3$

- Average speed $= \dfrac{\text{total distance}}{\text{total time}}$

- Density $= \dfrac{\text{mass}}{\text{volume}}$

7 Congruence, constructions and loci

7.1 Congruence

■ **Congruent means being the same size and shape, but not necessarily the same way round.**

In particular, triangles are certain to be congruent if one of four conditions can be shown to exist:

All three sides are the same (SSS).

Two sides and the included angle are the same (SAS).

Two angles and the included side are the same (ASA).

Both triangles have a right angle, the hypotenuses are equal and one pair of corresponding sides is equal (RHS).

Two triangles with the same angles could be different sizes. Also, having two sides and an angle the same does not prove congruence if the angle is not the one included between the sides.

Example 1
Prove that the base angles of an isosceles triangle are equal.

In the isosceles triangle, bisect angle A:

$$AB = AC \qquad \text{(the equal sides)}$$
$$AX = AX \qquad \text{(the same side)}$$
$$BAX = CAX \qquad \text{(angle } A \text{ was bisected)}$$

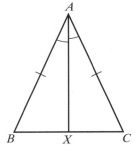

Therefore triangles AXB and AXC are congruent (SAS).

Therefore angle B = angle C.

This result can also be proved by joining A to the mid-point of BC (using SSS) or by drawing a perpendicular from A to BC (using RHS).

Example 2
Prove that the perpendicular to a chord from the centre of a circle bisects the chord.

In triangles OAX and OBX

$$AO = BO \qquad \text{radii of the circle}$$
$$OX = OX \qquad \text{same line}$$
$$\angle OXA = \angle OXB \qquad 90° \ (OX \text{ is perpendicular to } AB)$$

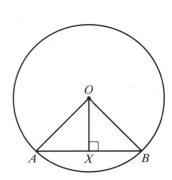

Therefore triangles OAX, OBX are congruent (*RHS*)

Hence $AX = BX$

Exercise 7A   **Links 3E**

1   *ABCD* is a rectangle. Prove triangles *ADC*
    and *BCD* are congruent.

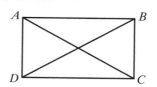

2   *PQRS* is a parallelogram. Prove triangles *SXR*
    and *QXP* are congruent.

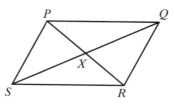

3   In the diagram *D* and *E* are mid-points.
    FC is parallel to *BA*.
    Prove triangles *DAE* and *FCE* are
    congruent.

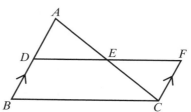

4   *ABCDE* is a regular pentagon.
    Prove triangles *EAB* and *BCD*
    are congruent.

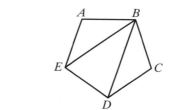

5   In the diagram triangles
    ABC and *AXY* are isosceles.
    Prove triangles *BXA* and *CYA*
    are congruent.

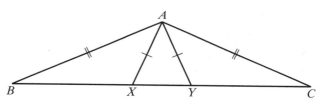

6   *WXYZ* is a kite.
    Prove triangles *WZY* and *WXY*
    are congruent.

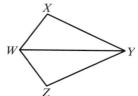

7   *ABCD* is a square.
    CXB and *BXY* are equilateral triangles.
    Show that triangles *ABY* and *ABX*
    are congruent.

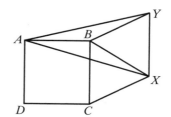

8   Prove that the line joining the mid-point of a chord to the
    centre of the circle is perpendicular to the chord.

7.2 Constructions

Example 3

(a) *ABCD* is a rhombus. Prove *BD* bisects angle *ADC*.

(b) If you now join *AC* so that *AC* and *DB* cross at *M*, show triangles *DAM* and *DCM* are congruent. What do you now know about the angles at *M* and the lengths *AM* and *MC*?

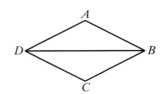

(a) In triangles *DAB* and *DCB*:

$$DA = DC \qquad \text{(sides of a rhombus are equal)}$$
$$AB = BC \qquad \text{(sides of a rhombus are equal)}$$
$$DB = DB \qquad \text{(same)}$$

Therefore the triangles are congruent.
Hence angle *ADB* = angle *CDB*
i.e. *BD* bisects angle *ADC*.

(b)
$$DA = DC \qquad\qquad \text{(sides of a rhombus are equal)}$$
$$DM = DM \qquad\qquad \text{(same)}$$
angle *ADM* = angle *CDM* (just proved)

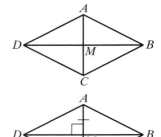

Hence the triangles are congruent (SAS).

Therefore angle *AMD* = angle *CMD* = 90° and *AM* = *MC*.

■ **A formal construction is an accurate drawing carried out using a straight edge (ruler), pencil and compasses.**

The rhombus is the foundation for all the basic constructions:
(i)   bisecting an angle
(ii)   bisecting a line (with a perpendicular bisector)
(iii) creating a perpendicular.

Example 4

(a) Bisect an angle *BAC*   (b) Construct the perpendicular bisector of a line *AB*

(a) With centre *A*, mark equal arcs at *B* and *C*.

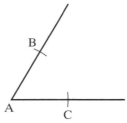

Using *B* and *C* as centres, locate the vertex that completes a rhombus by drawing intersecting arcs.

Draw the bisector.

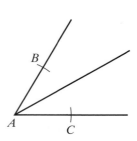

(ii) *AB* is to be the diameter of a rhombus and the
     perpendicular bisector will be the other diagonal.

     With *A* and *B* as centres, and the compasses fixed,
     draw intersecting arcs above and below *AB* to locate
     the other vertices of the rhombus.

     Draw the perpendicular bisector.

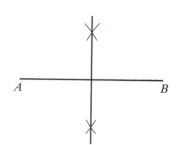

Example 5

Using ruler, pencil and compasses,
construct the shape *ABCD*.

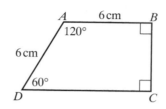

Step 1   Draw *AD*:

Step 2   Create an equilateral triangle:

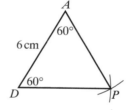

Compasses set at 6 cm
using *A* and *D* as centres.

Step 3   Create a second
         equilateral triangle:

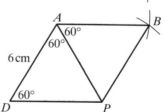

Compasses set at 6 cm
using *A* and *P* as centres.

Step 4   Construct a
         perpendicular
         to *AB* at *B*:

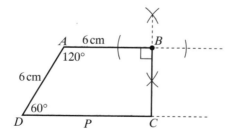

Extend *AB* and *DP*. With *B* as
centre, draw equal arcs on *AB*
produced. Using these new
centres, draw two sets of
intersecting arcs above and below
B. You now have the vertices of a
rhombus. Use the diagonal
perpendicular to *AB* to draw *BC*.

Note: Bisecting a right angle (from a perpendicular) produces 45°, $22\frac{1}{2}°$, etc.
       Bisecting 60° (from an equilateral triangle) produces 30°, 15°, etc.
       Combinations of the above allow any multiple of $7\frac{1}{2}°$ to be created.

Exercise 7B   **Links 6K**

In these questions, use ruler and compass constructions.
Protractors are not allowed.

1   Construct angles of 30°, 45° and 15°.

2   Construct accurate drawings of these diagrams:

(a)
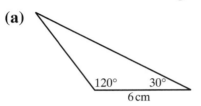

(b)
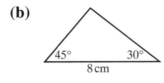

(c)
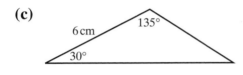

(d)
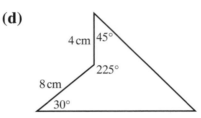

3   Construct these diagrams accurately:

(a)
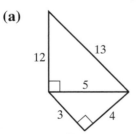

(b)
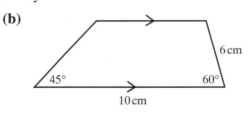

4   Construct a square with side 8 cm.

5   Construct accurate drawings of these triangles:

(a)
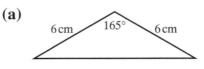

(b)
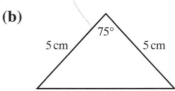

7.3 Loci

■ **A locus is a set of points obeying a particular rule.**

There are four important situations in two dimensions:

1 The locus of points which are a constant distance from a fixed point is a circle.

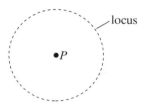

2 The locus of points which are equidistant from two fixed points is the perpendicular bisector.

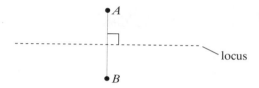

3 The locus of points which are equidistant from a pair of intersecting line segments is the bisector.

4 The locus of points which are a fixed distance from a line is a pair of parallel lines.

For a line segment there would be a semicircle on each end.

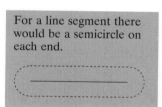

Example 6

ABCD is a trapezium. Shade the points which are nearer *DC* than *AD* and nearer *D* than *C*.

(i) To be nearer *DC* than *AC* you need the line which bisects angle *D*.

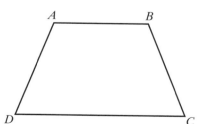

(ii) To be nearer D than C you need the perpendicular bisector of DC.

(iii) Shade the area which is nearer DC than DA and nearer D than C.

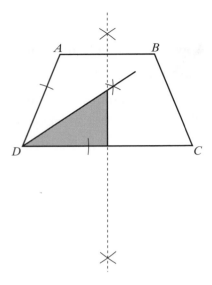

Exercise 7C   **Links 6J**

1 Copy the diagram and draw the locus of the points outside the rectangle that are 3 centimetres from the edges of the rectangle.

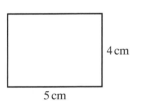

4 cm

5 cm

2 Points A and B are 8 cm apart.
Make an accurate drawing to show all the points that are less than 6 cm from A but nearer to B than A.

3

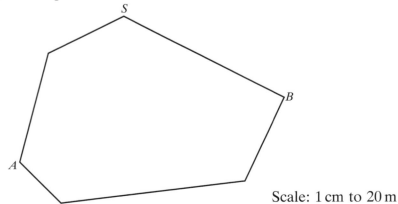

$ABCD$ is the plan of a room. Copy the diagram and shade all the points that are nearer wall DC than AD. Use a scale of $1:50$.

4 The diagram is a plan of a field drawn to a scale of 1 cm to 20 m.

Scale: 1 cm to 20 m

There is a water sprinkler at *S*.
The sprinkler can water that region of the field which is
60 metres or less from the sprinkler.
(a) Copy the diagram and shade the region of the field which
is 60 metres or less from the sprinkler.

A farmer is going to lay a pipe to help water the field.
A and *B* are posts which mark the widest part of the field.
The pipe will cross the field so that it is always the same
distance from *A* as it is from *B*.
(b) On the diagram draw a line accurately to show where the
pipe should be laid. (E)

5   Triangle *ABC* is shown on
the diagram.

(a) Copy the diagram and draw accurately the locus of the
points which are 1.5 cm from *B*.
(b) On the diagram, draw accurately the locus of the points
which are the same distance from *BA* as they are from
BC.

T is a point inside triangle *ABC*.
T is 1.5 cm from *B*.
T is the same distance from *BA* as it is from *BC*.

(c) On the diagram, mark the point *T* clearly with a cross.
Label it with the letter *T*.

Summary of key points

■ Congruent means being the same size and shape, but not
necessarily the same way round.

■ A formal construction is an accurate drawing carried out
using a straight edge (ruler), pencil and compasses.

■ A locus is a set of points obeying a particular rule.

8 Transformations

8.1 Properties of transformations

■ A reflection produces a mirror image in a line of symmetry.

You describe a reflection by giving the equation of the mirror line.

The object and image are congruent.

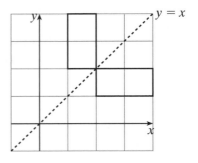

■ A rotation is described by giving
  ● centre of rotation
  ● amount of turn
  ● direction of turn.
  The object and image are congruent.

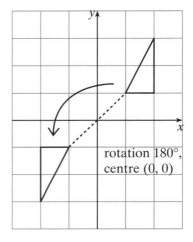

rotation 180°, centre (0, 0)

■ An enlargement is described by giving
  ● the centre of enlargement
  ● the scale factor.
  The object and image are similar but not congruent.

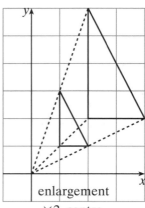

enlargement ×2, centre the origin

■ A translation moves every point on a shape the same distance and direction.

A translation is described by a vector $\begin{pmatrix} x \\ y \end{pmatrix}$.

The object and image are congruent.

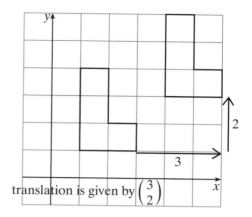

translation is given by $\begin{pmatrix} 3 \\ 2 \end{pmatrix}$

Exercise 8A

1 List what happens to
  (a) angles   **(b)** lengths of sides
  under the transformations of
  (i) reflection
  (ii) rotation
  (iii) enlargement
  (iv) translation.

8.2 Combined transformations

■ **Transformations can be combined by performing one transformation and then performing another transformation on the image.**

Example 1
(a) Reflect the shape in the x-axis.
(b) Reflect the image in the line $y = x$.
(c) Describe the single transformation which is equivalent to a combination of these two transformations.

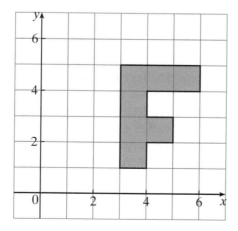

(a)

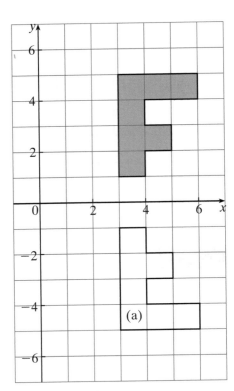

(b)

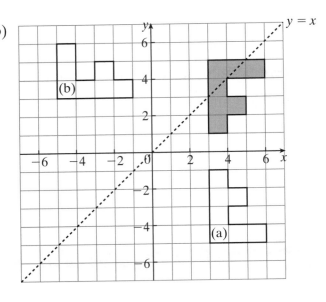

(c) The single transformation is a rotation through 90°
anticlockwise about the origin.

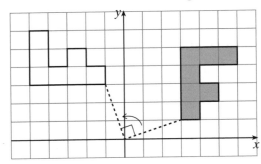

Example 2

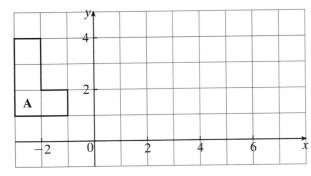

(a) Reflect the shape **A** in the y-axis.
Call it **B**.
(b) Reflect the image in the line $x = 4$;
call it **C**.
(c) Describe the single transformation which
maps **A** onto **C**.

(a)

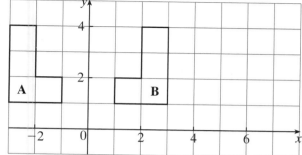

(b)

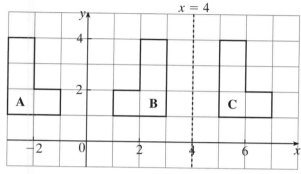

(c) The single transformation which maps **A** onto **C** is a translation $\begin{pmatrix} 8 \\ 0 \end{pmatrix}$.

■ **A reflection followed by a reflection can be replaced by the single transformation of**
  • **a rotation if the reflection lines are not parallel**
  • **a translation if the reflection lines are parallel.**

Exercise 8B   Links (*6G*) 6G

1 Copy the triangle onto graph paper.
  (a) Reflect the triangle in the *y*-axis.
  (b) Reflect the image in the *x*-axis.
  (c) Describe the single transformation which replaces **(a)** and **(b)**.

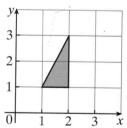

2 Copy the flag onto graph paper.
  (a) Reflect the flag in the *x*-axis.
  (b) Reflect the image in the line $y = 2$.
  (c) Describe the single transformation that replaces **(a)** and **(b)**.

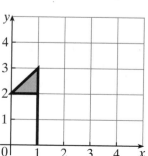

3 Copy and complete the coordinate grid so that x goes from
−4 to 4 and y goes from −4 to 4. Copy the triangle **A**.
(a) Reflect **A** in the x-axis. Label it **B**.
(b) Rotate **A** through $\frac{1}{2}$ turn about the origin. Label it **C**.
(c) Describe fully the transformation which maps **B** onto **C**.

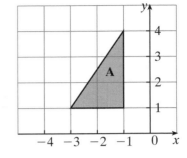

4 Copy and complete the coordinate grid so that x and y
both go from −10 to 10. Copy the rectangle **D**.
(a) Enlarge the rectangle **D** with centre of
enlargement $(0, 0)$, scale factor −1.
(b) Describe this transformation in another way.

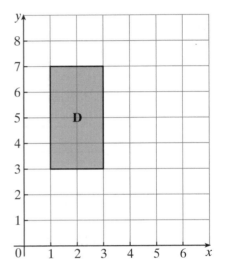

5 (a) Start with the same flag as question **2**.
Reflect the flag in the line $y = x$.
(b) Rotate the image 90° anticlockwise about the origin.
(c) Describe the single transformation that replaces (a) and (b).

6 (a) Start with the same triangle as question **3**.
Rotate the triangle through −90° about the centre $(0, 0)$.
(b) Reflect the image in the line $y = x$.
(c) Describe the single transformation that replaces (a) and (b).

> Remember: −90° is the
> same as 90° clockwise.

Summary of key points

- **A reflection produces a mirror image in a line
  of symmetry.**

  **You describe a reflection by giving the equation
  of the mirror line.**

  The object and image are congruent.

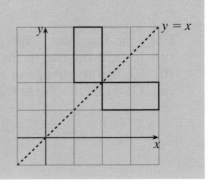

- A rotation is described by giving
  - centre of rotation
  - amount of turn
  - direction of turn.

  The object and image are congruent.

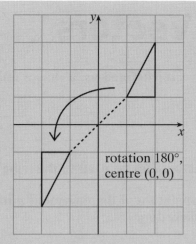

rotation 180°, centre (0, 0)

- An enlargement is described by giving
  - the centre of enlargement
  - the scale factor.

  The object and image are similar but not congruent.

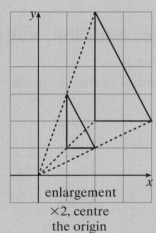

enlargement ×2, centre the origin

- A translation moves every point on a shape the same distance and direction. A translation is described by a

  vector $\begin{pmatrix} x \\ y \end{pmatrix}$.

  The object and image are congruent.

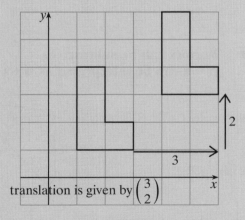

translation is given by $\begin{pmatrix} 3 \\ 2 \end{pmatrix}$

- Transformations can be combined by performing one transformation and then performing another transformation on the image.

- A reflection followed by a reflection can be replaced by the single transformation of
  - a rotation if the reflection lines are not parallel
  - a translation if the reflection lines are parallel.

9 Vectors

■ A vector defined as 'a' has a unique length and direction.

■ Vectors can be used to describe translations e.g. $\begin{pmatrix} p \\ q \end{pmatrix}$ is a translation of displacement p in the x-direction and q in the y-direction.

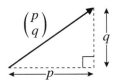

9.1 Vector addition, subtraction and scalars

■ $\mathbf{a} + \mathbf{b} = \mathbf{b} + \mathbf{a}$
■ The resultant of the vectors **a** and **b** is the vector **a + b**.

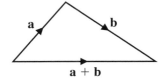

e.g. $\begin{pmatrix} 3 \\ 2 \end{pmatrix} + \begin{pmatrix} 4 \\ -3 \end{pmatrix} = \begin{pmatrix} 7 \\ -1 \end{pmatrix}$

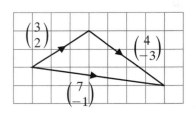

■ Vectors can be subtracted.
  p − q can be interpreted as **p + (−q)**.

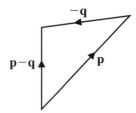

e.g. $\begin{pmatrix} 4 \\ 5 \end{pmatrix} - \begin{pmatrix} 2 \\ 4 \end{pmatrix} = \begin{pmatrix} 4 \\ 5 \end{pmatrix} + \begin{pmatrix} -2 \\ -4 \end{pmatrix} = \begin{pmatrix} 4-2 \\ 5-4 \end{pmatrix} = \begin{pmatrix} 2 \\ 1 \end{pmatrix}$

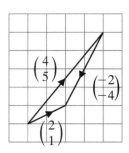

■ A vector $k\mathbf{a}$ is parallel to **a** and k times **a**.

For the vector $\begin{pmatrix} p \\ q \end{pmatrix}$, $k \times \begin{pmatrix} p \\ q \end{pmatrix} = \begin{pmatrix} kp \\ kq \end{pmatrix}$.

k is called the scalar and is a number.

e.g. $4\begin{pmatrix} 1 \\ 2 \end{pmatrix} = \begin{pmatrix} 4 \times 1 \\ 4 \times 2 \end{pmatrix} = \begin{pmatrix} 4 \\ 8 \end{pmatrix}$

■ Another way to consider the addition and subtraction of two vectors is by using the parallelogram method.

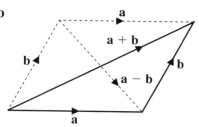

■ $\mathbf{a} + (\mathbf{b} + \mathbf{c}) = (\mathbf{a} + \mathbf{b}) + \mathbf{c}$
■ $k(\mathbf{a} + \mathbf{b}) = k\mathbf{a} + k\mathbf{b}$
■ $(p + q)\mathbf{a} = p\mathbf{a} + q\mathbf{a}$

for any vectors **a**, **b** and **c** and any scalars p, q and k.

Example 1

A is the point $(3, -1)$ and B the point $(5, 3)$.

$$\overrightarrow{AC} = \begin{pmatrix} 1 \\ 3 \end{pmatrix}.$$

$\overrightarrow{AC}$ is another way of writing down 'the vector starting at A and finishing at C'.

Write down the column vector

(a) $\overrightarrow{AB}$,

(b) $\overrightarrow{BA}$.

(c) Write down the coordinates of C.

(a) $\begin{pmatrix} 2 \\ 4 \end{pmatrix}$

(b) $\begin{pmatrix} -2 \\ -4 \end{pmatrix}$

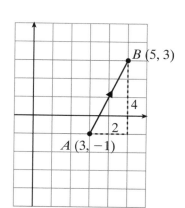

$$\overrightarrow{AB} = \begin{pmatrix} 2 \\ 4 \end{pmatrix}$$

(c) (4, 2)

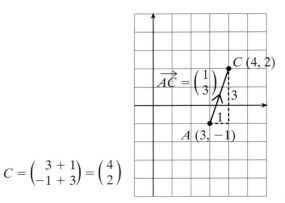

$$C = \begin{pmatrix} 3+1 \\ -1+3 \end{pmatrix} = \begin{pmatrix} 4 \\ 2 \end{pmatrix}$$

Example 2

$$\mathbf{m} = \begin{pmatrix} 2 \\ -1 \end{pmatrix}, \ \mathbf{n} = \begin{pmatrix} 3 \\ -4 \end{pmatrix}$$

(a) Write as column vectors
    (i) $\mathbf{m} + \mathbf{n}$ (ii) $\mathbf{m} - \mathbf{n}$ (iii) $3\mathbf{n}$ (iv) $2\mathbf{m} - 3\mathbf{n}$

(b) Find the vector $\mathbf{y}$ such that $\mathbf{m} + 2\mathbf{y} = \mathbf{n}$.

(a) (i) $\mathbf{m} + \mathbf{n} = \begin{pmatrix} 2 \\ -1 \end{pmatrix} + \begin{pmatrix} 3 \\ -4 \end{pmatrix} = \begin{pmatrix} 2+3 \\ -1+-4 \end{pmatrix} = \begin{pmatrix} 5 \\ -5 \end{pmatrix}$

    (ii) $\mathbf{m} - \mathbf{n} = \begin{pmatrix} 2 \\ -1 \end{pmatrix} - \begin{pmatrix} 3 \\ -4 \end{pmatrix} = \begin{pmatrix} 2-3 \\ -1--4 \end{pmatrix} = \begin{pmatrix} -1 \\ 3 \end{pmatrix}$

    (iii) $3\mathbf{n} = 3 \times \begin{pmatrix} 3 \\ -4 \end{pmatrix} = \begin{pmatrix} 9 \\ -12 \end{pmatrix}$

    (iv) $2\mathbf{m} - 3\mathbf{n} = 2 \times \begin{pmatrix} 2 \\ -1 \end{pmatrix} - \begin{pmatrix} 9 \\ -12 \end{pmatrix} = \begin{pmatrix} 4 \\ -2 \end{pmatrix} - \begin{pmatrix} 9 \\ -12 \end{pmatrix}$

$$= \begin{pmatrix} 4-9 \\ -2--12 \end{pmatrix} = \begin{pmatrix} -5 \\ 10 \end{pmatrix}$$

(b) $\mathbf{m} + 2\mathbf{y} = \mathbf{n}$

    So $2\mathbf{y} = \mathbf{n} - \mathbf{m}$

$$= \begin{pmatrix} 3 \\ -4 \end{pmatrix} - \begin{pmatrix} 2 \\ -1 \end{pmatrix} = \begin{pmatrix} 3-2 \\ -4--1 \end{pmatrix}$$

$$2\mathbf{y} = \begin{pmatrix} 1 \\ -3 \end{pmatrix}$$

    So $\mathbf{y} = \frac{1}{2}\begin{pmatrix} 1 \\ -3 \end{pmatrix} = \begin{pmatrix} \frac{1}{2} \\ -1\frac{1}{2} \end{pmatrix}$

Exercise 9A   **Links (26A, 26B) 25A, 25B**

1 A is the point $(2, 4)$, B is the point $(-1, 5)$ and C is the point $(-2, -4)$.
Write down the column vectors

    (a) $\overrightarrow{AB}$ **(b)** $\overrightarrow{BA}$ **(c)** $\overrightarrow{AC}$ **(d)** $\overrightarrow{BC}$

2 A is the point $(0, 3)$ and B is the point $(-2, 5)$. $\overrightarrow{AC} = \begin{pmatrix} 2 \\ 5 \end{pmatrix}$.

    (a) Write down the column vectors
        (i) $\overrightarrow{AB}$ **(ii)** $\overrightarrow{BA}$.
    (b) Write down the coordinates of C.

3 $\overrightarrow{AB}$ is the vector $\begin{pmatrix} 5 \\ -1 \end{pmatrix}$ and $\overrightarrow{BC}$ is the vector $\begin{pmatrix} 2 \\ 3 \end{pmatrix}$.

    (a) Work out the vector $\overrightarrow{AC}$.
    (b) Draw a diagram to illustrate your answer.

4 $\mathbf{m} = \begin{pmatrix} 3 \\ 2 \end{pmatrix}$ $\mathbf{n} = \begin{pmatrix} 2 \\ -5 \end{pmatrix}$

    (a) Work out and   **(b)** show graphically:
    (i) $\mathbf{m} + \mathbf{n}$ **(ii)** $\mathbf{m} - \mathbf{n}$ **(iii)** $3\mathbf{m}$ **(iv)** $2\mathbf{n}$ **(v)** $3\mathbf{m} - 2\mathbf{n}$

5 $\mathbf{a} = \begin{pmatrix} 1 \\ 3 \end{pmatrix}$ $\mathbf{b} = \begin{pmatrix} 3 \\ 2 \end{pmatrix}$

    Work out the resultant vectors of:
    (a) $3\mathbf{a} - 2\mathbf{b}$
    (b) $2\mathbf{b} - 3\mathbf{a}$.
    (c) Find the vector $\mathbf{x}$ such that $\mathbf{a} + 2\mathbf{x} = \mathbf{b}$.

6 $\mathbf{a} = \begin{pmatrix} 2 \\ 5 \end{pmatrix}$ $\mathbf{b} = \begin{pmatrix} 1 \\ 1 \end{pmatrix}$

    Draw a diagram to show that
    (a) $3(\mathbf{a} + \mathbf{b}) = 3\mathbf{a} + 3\mathbf{b}$
    (b) $(3 + 4)\mathbf{a} = 3\mathbf{a} + 4\mathbf{a}$.

9.2 Linear combinations

■ **Combinations of the vectors a and b of the form $p\mathbf{a} + q\mathbf{b}$, where p and q are scalars, are called linear combinations of the vectors a and b.**

Example 3

$$\mathbf{a} = \begin{pmatrix} 3 \\ 2 \end{pmatrix} \qquad \mathbf{b} = \begin{pmatrix} 1 \\ -4 \end{pmatrix}$$

Calculate $\mathbf{x}$ given that $\mathbf{a} + \mathbf{x} = \mathbf{b}$.

$$\begin{pmatrix} 3 \\ 2 \end{pmatrix} + \mathbf{x} = \begin{pmatrix} 1 \\ -4 \end{pmatrix}$$

$$\mathbf{x} = \begin{pmatrix} 1 \\ -4 \end{pmatrix} - \begin{pmatrix} 3 \\ 2 \end{pmatrix}$$

$$\mathbf{x} = \begin{pmatrix} -2 \\ -6 \end{pmatrix}$$

Example 4

$$\mathbf{a} = \begin{pmatrix} 1 \\ 5 \end{pmatrix} \qquad \mathbf{b} = \begin{pmatrix} 3 \\ 2 \end{pmatrix}$$

(a) Find scalars p and q such that $p\mathbf{a} + q\mathbf{b}$ is parallel to the x-axis.
(b) Find scalars m and n such that $m\mathbf{a} + n\mathbf{b}$ is parallel to the y-axis.

(a) $p\mathbf{a} + q\mathbf{b} = p\begin{pmatrix} 1 \\ 5 \end{pmatrix} + q\begin{pmatrix} 3 \\ 2 \end{pmatrix}.$

To be parallel to the x-axis, the y-component of the vector must be zero.

$$\text{So } \quad p\begin{pmatrix} 1 \\ 5 \end{pmatrix} + q\begin{pmatrix} 3 \\ 2 \end{pmatrix} = \begin{pmatrix} \text{some value, say } x \\ 0 \end{pmatrix}$$

$$\begin{pmatrix} p + 3q \\ 5p + 2q \end{pmatrix} = \begin{pmatrix} x \\ 0 \end{pmatrix}$$

Then $5p + 2q = 0$
Two possible values are $p = 2$, $q = -5$
(so $2\mathbf{a} - 5\mathbf{b}$ is parallel to the x-axis).

> There are many other values.

(b) $m\mathbf{a} + n\mathbf{b} = m\begin{pmatrix} 1 \\ 5 \end{pmatrix} + n\begin{pmatrix} 3 \\ 2 \end{pmatrix}.$

To be parallel to the y-axis, the x-component of the vector must be zero.

$$\text{So } \quad m\begin{pmatrix} 1 \\ 5 \end{pmatrix} + n\begin{pmatrix} 3 \\ 2 \end{pmatrix} = \begin{pmatrix} 0 \\ y \end{pmatrix}$$

$$\begin{pmatrix} m + 3n \\ 5m + 2n \end{pmatrix} = \begin{pmatrix} 0 \\ y \end{pmatrix}$$

> y is some value.

Then $m + 3n = 0$
Two possible values are $m = 3$ and $n = -1$
so $3\mathbf{a} - \mathbf{b}$ is parallel to the y-axis.

Example 5

Find the values of the scalars p and q

when $p\begin{pmatrix} 5 \\ 2 \end{pmatrix} + q\begin{pmatrix} -1 \\ 4 \end{pmatrix} = \begin{pmatrix} 7 \\ 16 \end{pmatrix}.$

$$\begin{pmatrix} 5p \\ 2p \end{pmatrix} + \begin{pmatrix} -q \\ 4q \end{pmatrix} = \begin{pmatrix} 7 \\ 16 \end{pmatrix}$$

$$\begin{aligned} 5p - q &= 7 \quad &(1) \\ 2p + 4q &= 16 \quad &(2) \end{aligned}$$

> Solve these two simultaneous equations for p and q.

$$\begin{aligned} 4 \times (1): \quad 20p - 4q &= 28 \\ +(2): \quad 22p &= 44 \\ p &= 2 \end{aligned}$$

Substitute $p = 2$ into (1):
$$\begin{aligned} 5 \times 2 - q &= 7 \\ q &= 3 \end{aligned}$$

So $p = 2$ and $q = 3$.

Exercise 9B   Links (*26D*) 25D

1   $\mathbf{a} = \begin{pmatrix} 2 \\ -1 \end{pmatrix}$, $\mathbf{b} = \begin{pmatrix} 6 \\ 2 \end{pmatrix}$; calculate $\mathbf{x}$, given that $\mathbf{a} + \mathbf{x} = \mathbf{b}$.

2   $\mathbf{m} = \begin{pmatrix} 3 \\ -1 \end{pmatrix}$, $\mathbf{n} = \begin{pmatrix} 2 \\ -5 \end{pmatrix}$; calculate $\mathbf{y}$, given that $\mathbf{m} + \mathbf{y} = \mathbf{n}$.

3   $\mathbf{r} = \begin{pmatrix} 5 \\ -2 \end{pmatrix}$, $\mathbf{s} = \begin{pmatrix} -1 \\ 3 \end{pmatrix}$; calculate $\mathbf{z}$, given that $\mathbf{r} + \mathbf{z} = \mathbf{s}$.

4   $\mathbf{a} = \begin{pmatrix} 2 \\ 3 \end{pmatrix}$ $\mathbf{b} = \begin{pmatrix} 3 \\ 5 \end{pmatrix}$

   (a) Find scalars p and q such that $p\mathbf{a} + q\mathbf{b}$ is parallel to the x-axis.

   (b) Find scalars r and s such that $r\mathbf{a} + s\mathbf{b}$ is parallel to the y-axis.

5   $\mathbf{a} = \begin{pmatrix} 4 \\ -1 \end{pmatrix}$ $\mathbf{b} = \begin{pmatrix} 2 \\ 1 \end{pmatrix}$

   Given that $\mathbf{a} + p\mathbf{b}$ is parallel to the y-axis, find the value of p.

6   Find values of p and q when $p\begin{pmatrix}2\\1\end{pmatrix} + q\begin{pmatrix}3\\-1\end{pmatrix} = \begin{pmatrix}8\\1\end{pmatrix}$.

7   Find a linear combination of vectors $\mathbf{a} = \begin{pmatrix}2\\3\end{pmatrix}$ and $\mathbf{b} = \begin{pmatrix}-1\\2\end{pmatrix}$

which is equal to the vector $\begin{pmatrix}2\\5\end{pmatrix}$.

9.3 Position vectors

■   **The position vector of a point P is $\overrightarrow{OP}$, where O is usually the origin.**

e.g. $\overrightarrow{OP}$ is position vector $\begin{pmatrix}2\\3\end{pmatrix}$:

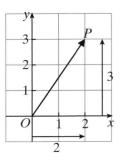

Example 6

A is the point $(2, 1)$ and B is the point $(4, 7)$.
Calculate the position vector of the mid-point of AB.

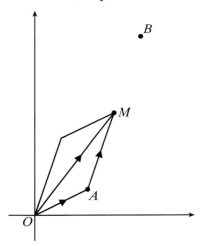

Let the mid-point of $AB = M$.
$\overrightarrow{OM}$ is the position vector of M.

By parallelogram of vectors (or triangle addition of vectors):

$$\overrightarrow{OA} + \overrightarrow{AM} = \overrightarrow{OM}$$

So $\begin{pmatrix}2\\1\end{pmatrix} + \tfrac{1}{2}\begin{pmatrix}2\\6\end{pmatrix} = \overrightarrow{OM}$

$\begin{pmatrix}2\\1\end{pmatrix} + \begin{pmatrix}1\\3\end{pmatrix} = \overrightarrow{OM}$

$$\overrightarrow{OM} = \begin{pmatrix}3\\4\end{pmatrix}$$

$\overrightarrow{AM} = \tfrac{1}{2}\overrightarrow{AB}$
so
$\overrightarrow{AM} = \tfrac{1}{2}\begin{pmatrix}2\\6\end{pmatrix}$

Example 7

The position vector of $A = \mathbf{a}$.
The position vector of $B = \mathbf{b}$.
C lies on the line AB and $AC = \frac{1}{3}CB$.
Find the position vector of C.

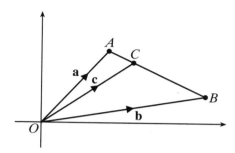

$$\overrightarrow{AC} = \tfrac{1}{4}\overrightarrow{AB}$$

where $\overrightarrow{AB} = \mathbf{b} - \mathbf{a}$ (By parallelogram of vector)

then $\overrightarrow{AC} = \tfrac{1}{4}(\mathbf{b} - \mathbf{a})$

Let $\mathbf{c} = \overrightarrow{OC}$

$$= \overrightarrow{OA} + \overrightarrow{AC}$$

$$= \mathbf{a} + \tfrac{1}{4}(\mathbf{b} - \mathbf{a})$$

$$= \tfrac{3}{4}\mathbf{a} + \tfrac{1}{4}\mathbf{b}$$

■   **If A and B have position vectors $\mathbf{a}$ and $\mathbf{b}$ respectively then the vector**

$$\overrightarrow{AB} = \mathbf{b} - \mathbf{a}$$

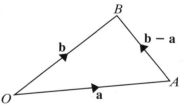

■   **If A and B have position vectors $\mathbf{a}$ and $\mathbf{b}$ then the position vector of the mid-point, M, of the line joining A to B is**

$$\overrightarrow{OM} = \mathbf{m} = \tfrac{1}{2}(\mathbf{a} + \mathbf{b})$$

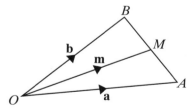

Exercise 9C   Links *(26E)* 25E

1 A is the point $(2, 3)$ and B is the point $(8, 7)$.
Calculate the position vector of the mid-point of AB.

2   The position vector of $A = \mathbf{a}$.
The position vector of $B = \mathbf{b}$.
C lies on the line AB and $AC = \frac{1}{4}CB$.
Find the position vector of C.

3 A is the point $(3, -3)$ and B is the point $(9, 3)$.
C lies on the line AB, such that $AC = \frac{1}{2}CB$.
Calculate the coordinates of C.

4 D is the point $(3, 2)$, E is the point $(2, 5)$ and F is the point $(-1, -1)$.
   (a) Find the coordinates of the mid-points of
   (i) DE **(ii)** DF **(iii)** EF.
   (b) G lies on DE extended so that $DG = 2 \times DE$.
   Calculate the coordinates of G.

5 $ABCD$ is a parallelogram with $A\,(-5, 5)$, $B\,(-4, 8)$ and $C\,(-4, 2)$. Write down the position vector of D and the mid-point of BD.

9.4 Proving geometrical results

Example 8
Prove that the diagonals of a rhombus bisect each other.

In rhombus $OACB$

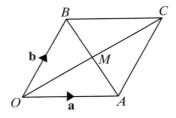

$$\overrightarrow{OA} = \mathbf{a}$$
$$\overrightarrow{OB} = \mathbf{b}$$

Opposite sides are parallel and equal so

$$\overrightarrow{BC} = \mathbf{a}$$
$$\overrightarrow{AC} = \mathbf{b}$$

So

$$\overrightarrow{OC} = \overrightarrow{OA} + \overrightarrow{AC}$$
$$= \mathbf{a} + \mathbf{b}$$

If M is the mid-point of $\overrightarrow{OC}$

$$\overrightarrow{OM} = \frac{1}{2}\overrightarrow{OC}$$
$$= \frac{1}{2}(\mathbf{a} + \mathbf{b})$$

but $\frac{1}{2}(\mathbf{a} + \mathbf{b})$ is the position vector of the mid-point of AB.
So OC bisects AB.

Exercise 9D   **Mixed questions**

1 A is the point $(1, 3)$, B is the point $(-2, 4)$ and C is the point $(5, -7)$.
Write down the column vectors
   (a) $\overrightarrow{AB}$ **(b)** $\overrightarrow{AC}$ **(c)** $\overrightarrow{CA}$ **(d)** $\overrightarrow{BC}$

2 $\mathbf{a} = \begin{pmatrix} 5 \\ 3 \end{pmatrix}$ $\mathbf{b} = \begin{pmatrix} -2 \\ 3 \end{pmatrix}$
Work out
   (a) $\mathbf{a} + \mathbf{b}$ **(b)** $\mathbf{b} - \mathbf{a}$ **(c)** $3\mathbf{b}$ **(d)** $2\mathbf{a} - 3\mathbf{b}$

3 $\mathbf{a} = \begin{pmatrix} 3 \\ 1 \end{pmatrix}$ $\mathbf{b} = \begin{pmatrix} 4 \\ 3 \end{pmatrix}$
Work out
   (a) $3\mathbf{a} - 2\mathbf{b}$,
   (b) $4\mathbf{b} - \mathbf{a}$.
   (c) Find the vector $\mathbf{x}$ such that $\mathbf{a} + 2\mathbf{x} = \mathbf{b}$.

4 $\mathbf{a} = \begin{pmatrix} 3 \\ -2 \end{pmatrix}$, $\mathbf{b} = \begin{pmatrix} -1 \\ 3 \end{pmatrix}$; calculate $\mathbf{x}$ given that $\mathbf{a} + \mathbf{x} = \mathbf{b}$.

5 $\mathbf{a} = \begin{pmatrix} 5 \\ -2 \end{pmatrix}$ $\mathbf{b} = \begin{pmatrix} 3 \\ 1 \end{pmatrix}$
Find scalars p and q such that $p\mathbf{a} + q\mathbf{b}$ is parallel to the y-axis.

6   Find values of p and q such that
$$p\begin{pmatrix} -1 \\ 2 \end{pmatrix} + q\begin{pmatrix} 2 \\ 3 \end{pmatrix} = \begin{pmatrix} 4 \\ 13 \end{pmatrix}$$

7   The position vector of $A = \mathbf{a}$.
The position vector of $B = \mathbf{b}$.
C is a point on AB such that $AC = \frac{1}{2}CB$.
Find the position vector of C.

8 M and N are the mid-points of the sides OA and OB of a triangle.
Prove that the line AB is parallel to the line MN and equal to twice the length of MN.

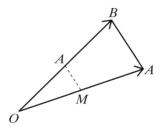

9   In triangle ABC, M is the mid-point of BC and N is the mid-point of AC.
$\overrightarrow{AB} = \mathbf{b}$ and $\overrightarrow{BC} = \mathbf{c}$.
BN is produced to a point D so that $BD:BN = 4:3$.
   (a) Write $\overrightarrow{AM}$ and $\overrightarrow{DC}$ in terms of $\mathbf{b}$ and $\mathbf{c}$.
   (b) Prove that AM is parallel to DC and $AM:DC = 3:2$.

Summary of key points

- A vector defined as 'a' has a unique length and direction.

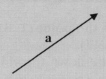

- Vectors can be used to describe translations e.g. $\begin{pmatrix} p \\ q \end{pmatrix}$ is a translation of displacement p in the x-direction and q in the y-direction.

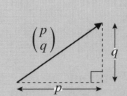

- $a + b = b + a$

- The resultant of the vectors **a** and **b** is the vector $a + b$.

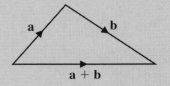

- Vectors can be subtracted.

- A vector $k\mathbf{a}$ is parallel to **a** and k times **a**.

  For the vector $\begin{pmatrix} p \\ q \end{pmatrix}$, $k \times \begin{pmatrix} p \\ q \end{pmatrix} = \begin{pmatrix} kp \\ kq \end{pmatrix}$.

- The parallelogram method is shown in the diagram:

- $a + (b + c) = (a + b) + c$

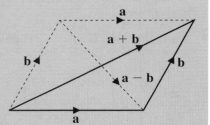

- $k(a + b) = ka + kb$

- $(p + q)a = pa + qa$

- Combinations of the vectors **a** and **b** of the form $p\mathbf{a} + q\mathbf{b}$, where p and q are scalars, are called linear combinations of the vectors **a** and **b**.

- The position vector of a point P is $\overrightarrow{OP}$, where O is usually the origin.

- If A and B have position vectors **a** and **b** respectively then the vector
$$\overrightarrow{AB} = b - a$$

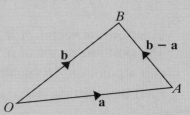

- If A and B have position vectors **a** and **b** then the position vector of the mid-point, M, of the line joining A to B is
$$\overrightarrow{OM} = \mathbf{m} = \tfrac{1}{2}(a + b)$$

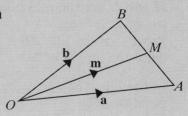

10 Handling data: probability and frequency density

10.1 Measures of probability

- $\text{P(event)} = \dfrac{\text{number of ways the event can occur}}{\text{total number of equally likely possibilities}}$

- $\text{Relative frequency} = \dfrac{\text{number of times event occurs}}{\text{total number of trials}}$

- **As the number of trials increases, the relative frequency approaches the probability of the event or outcome.**

Example 1

The diagram represents a regular octagonal spinner.
The spinner is to be spun once.

Work out the probability of the spinner stopping on

(a) the letter B   (b) the letter D   (c) a vowel

(a) The spinner has 8 edges; 3 labelled A, 2 labelled D and 1 labelled each of B, C and E.

So $\text{P(B)} = \frac{1}{8}$

(b) $\text{P(D)} = \frac{2}{8}$

(c) Of the letters A, B, C, D and E the vowels are A and E.
A and E occupy a total of 4 edges out of 8.

So $\text{P(vowel)} = \frac{4}{8} = \frac{1}{2}$

Example 2

There are four candidates in an election. Their names are

    Preston, Roberts, Smith, Taylor

Before the election a market research company asked a random sample of 1200 people which person they intended to vote for in the election. The response to the survey was as follows:

Preston	Roberts	Smith	Taylor
317	452	203	228

In the actual election 24 850 votes will be cast.

Work out, with a reason, an estimate of the likely number of votes that will be cast for Roberts.

The estimated probability of a vote being cast for Roberts $= \dfrac{452}{1200} = 0.376\,666.$

So our estimated $P(R) = 0.376\,666.$

But $P(R) = \dfrac{\text{no. of votes cast for Roberts}}{\text{total number of votes cast}} = \dfrac{\text{no. of votes cast for Roberts}}{24\,850}$

So likely number of votes cast for Roberts $= 24\,850 \times 0.376\,666$
$$= 9360.1666$$

i.e. since it must be a whole number (of votes) the likely number of votes to be cast for Roberts is 9360.

Exercise 10A   **Links 9A, 9B, 9C**

1   A bag contains 20 equal-sized number cards.
    Five of the cards have the number 2 written on them, two have
    the number 3, three have the number 4, six have the number 5
    and the remainder have the number 6.
    A number card is to be selected at random.
    Work out the probability of the selected card
    (a) showing the number 6,
    (b) showing an even number,
    (c) showing a prime number,
    (d) showing a multiple of 3.

2   A train is defined as being late if it arrives at the station 3 or
    more minutes after its scheduled arrival time.
    Explain how you could work out an estimate for the
    probability of a train being late.

3   Jane is conducting a survey into the number of goals scored in
    first-class football matches. She has data on 200 matches, as
    shown below:

Number of goals	0	1	2	3	4	5	6	7
Number of matches	7	23	36	96	22	9	6	1

   (a) Work out, with a reason, an estimate for the probability of
       a first-class football match finishing with
       (i)   exactly 4 goals being scored
       (ii) 4 or more goals being scored.
   During a season, 5200 first-class football matches will be
   played.
   (b) Work out an estimate for the most likely number of
       games to be played in which exactly three goals will be
       scored.

4   The diagram represents a biased pentagonal spinner with sections labelled A, B, C, D and E.
When the spinner is spun once, the probabilities of it stopping on each of the letters is given in the table below:

Letter	A	B	C	D	E
Probability	0.23	0.18	0.15	0.25	0.19

The spinner is to be spun 600 times.
Work out an estimate for the likely number of times it will stop on B.

10.2 Mutually exclusive and independent events

- Two events are **mutually exclusive** if the occurrence of one event means that the other cannot occur at the same time.

- When two events, A and B, are mutually exclusive

    P(A or B) = P(A) + P(B)

- Two events are **independent** when the occurrence of one neither affects nor is affected by the occurrence of the other.

- When two events are independent

    P(A and B) = P(A) × P(B)

Example 3

The diagram represents a biased pentagonal spinner with sections labelled with one of the letters A, B, C, D and E.
When the spinner is spun once the probabilities of it stopping on four of the sections are shown in the incomplete table below:

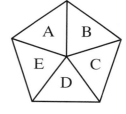

Section	A	B	C	D	E
Probability	0.23	0.16	0.19	0.24	

(a) Work out the probability of the spinner stopping on section E when it is spun once.

The spinner is to be spun once.

(b) Work out the probability that it will stop on either B or C.

The spinner is to be spun twice.

(c) Work out the probability of it stopping on section A both times.

(a) The sum of the probabilities must be 1, so

$$0.23 + 0.16 + 0.19 + 0.24 + P(E) = 1$$
$$0.82 + P(E) = 1$$
$$P(E) = 1 - 0.82$$
$$P(E) = 0.18$$

(b) The outcomes of stopping on A, B, C, D and E are all mutually exclusive, so

$$P(B \text{ or } C) = P(B) + P(C)$$
$$= 0.16 + 0.19$$
$$= 0.35$$

(c) The events of the first and second spin are independent. (What happens on the first spin has no bearing on the outcome of the second spin.)
The probability of stopping on A on both spins is the same as P(A and A):

$$P(A \text{ and } A) = P(A) \times P(A)$$
$$= 0.23 \times 0.23$$
$$= 0.0529$$

Example 4

Darren and James play a game of tennis followed by a game of darts.
The probability of Darren winning the game of tennis is 0.3.
The probability of Darren winning the game of darts is 0.2.

(a) Complete the probability tree diagram:

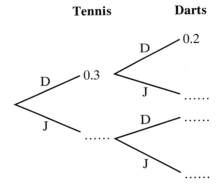

(b) Work out the probability of
(i) Darren winning the tennis and losing the darts,
(ii) James winning at least one game.

(a) The complete tree diagram is:

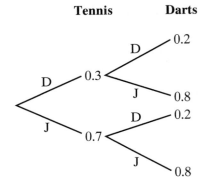

(b) (i) The probability of Darren winning the tennis and losing the darts can be worked out from this branch of the tree diagram:

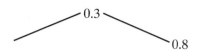

It is, then, $0.3 \times 0.8 = 0.24$

(ii) The probability of James winning at least one game is given by these three mutually exclusive branches of the tree diagram:

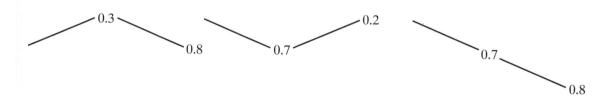

It is thus $(0.7 \times 0.2) + (0.3 \times 0.8) + (0.7 \times 0.8)$
$= 0.14 + 0.24 + 0.56 = 0.94$

(Note: the probability of James winning at least one game is equal to 1 minus the probability of James losing both games. James winning at least one game and James losing both games are exhaustive (all that can happen) and mutually exclusive. But the probability of James losing both games is equal to the probability of Darren winning both games. The probability of Darren winning both games is $0.3 \times 0.2 = 0.06$, so the probability of James winning at least one game is $1 - 0.06 = 0.94$.)

Exercise 10B   Links 9A, 9B, 9C, 9D

1   The probability that Sharon will pass her Science examination is 0.7.
The probability that she will pass her Music examination is 0.9.
Given that passing Music and passing Science are independent, work out the probability
(a) of Sharon passing both examinations,
(b) of Sharon passing Science and failing Music,
(c) of Sharon passing at least one of these examinations.

2   A cubical dice has each of its faces labelled with one of the
numbers 1, 2, 3, 4, 5 and 6.
The dice is biased.
When it is rolled once, the probabilities of it landing with each
face uppermost are given in the incomplete table below:

Face	1	2	3	4	5	6
Probability	0.18	0.13	0.21	0.17	0.16	

(a) Work out the probability of the dice landing with the face
labelled 6 uppermost when it is spun once.

The dice is to be spun twice.

(b) Work out the probability that it will land with
  (i)   the uppermost faces being 1 on each occasion,
  (ii)   the uppermost faces showing the same number on
         each occasion,
  (iii) the sum of the numbers on the uppermost faces
         being 4.

3   Sharon and Nicole are both due to take their driving test.
The probability that Sharon will pass is 0.8.
The probability that Nicole will pass is 0.6.
(a) Work out the probability of both girls passing the driving
test.
(b) Work out the probability of at least one of the girls
passing the driving test.

4   A bag contains five equal-sized beads. Three of these beads
are blue and two of them are red. A second bag contains eight
equal-sized beads. Three of these beads are blue and five of
them are red.
Asha selects, at random, one bead from each bag.
(a) Find the probability of each bead being blue.
(b) Find the probability of each bead being the same colour.
(c) Find the probability of each bead being a different colour.

5   England and Australia cricket teams toss an ordinary coin at
the start of each of the five test matches.
(a) Work out the probability that Australia will win the toss
on all five occasions.
(b) Work out the probability of England winning the toss at
least once.

6   The train leaves the station either **on time** or **late**.
   (a) Complete the probability tree diagram:

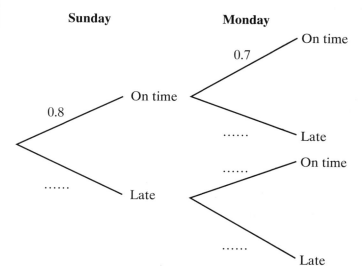

   (b) Work out the probability of the train being late on both days.
   (c) Work out the probability of the train being late at least
       once out of the two days.

7   Jenny has ten mugs. Six of the mugs are red and four are blue.
   In the morning she picks at random one mug from the ten
   mugs.
   In the afternoon she also picks one mug from the same ten
   mugs.
   (a) Complete the probability tree diagram:

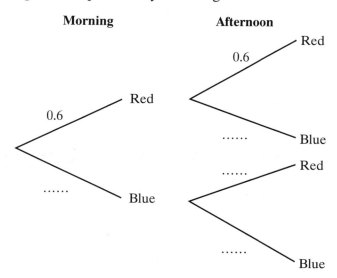

   (b) Work out the probability that Jenny will pick a red cup
       both in the morning and in the afternoon.
   (c) Work out the probability that Jenny will pick one of each
       colour of cup.

8 Lara is due to take her driving test. The probability that she will pass the test on the first occasion is 0.6. If she fails the test on the first occasion the probability of her passing on the second or any other occasion is 0.8.
Work out the probability of her passing the driving test within no more than two occasions.

10.3 Frequency density

■ Frequency density $= \dfrac{\text{frequency}}{\text{class width}}$

■ An alternative for frequency density is

$$\text{frequency density} = \dfrac{\text{frequency}}{\text{class width in standard class intervals}}$$

Example 5

The members of Karen's aerobics class are grouped by age.
The groupings are unequal class intervals, as in the table below:

Age (a, years) range	Frequency
$0 < a \leqslant 20$	12
$20 < a \leqslant 30$	15
$30 < a \leqslant 35$	15
$35 < a \leqslant 40$	20
$40 < a \leqslant 50$	10
$50 < a \leqslant 60$	12
$60 < a \leqslant 90$	9

Work out and tabulate the frequency densities
(a) using class widths   (b) using a standard class width of 5 years.

(a) Set up the table as follows:

Age (a, years) range	Class width (years)	Frequency	Frequency density
$0 < a \leqslant 20$	20	12	$\frac{12}{20} = 0.6$
$20 < a \leqslant 30$	10	15	$\frac{15}{10} = 1.5$
$30 < a \leqslant 35$	5	15	$\frac{15}{5} = 3$
$35 < a \leqslant 40$	5	20	$\frac{20}{5} = 4$
$40 < a \leqslant 50$	10	10	$\frac{10}{10} = 1$
$50 < a \leqslant 60$	10	12	$\frac{12}{10} = 1.2$
$60 < a \leqslant 90$	30	9	$\frac{9}{30} = 0.3$

(b) The standard class interval being set at 5 years means that a range such as $0 < a \leqslant 20$ or 20 years is 4 lots of the standard class interval. So we now repeat the table but in terms of standard class intervals:

Age (*a*, years) range	No. of st. class intervals	Frequency	Frequency density
$0 < a \leqslant 20$	4	12	$\frac{12}{4} = 3$
$20 < a \leqslant 30$	2	15	$\frac{15}{2} = 7.5$
$30 < a \leqslant 35$	1	15	$\frac{15}{1} = 15$
$35 < a \leqslant 40$	1	20	$\frac{20}{1} = 20$
$40 < a \leqslant 50$	2	10	$\frac{10}{2} = 5$
$50 < a \leqslant 60$	2	12	$\frac{12}{2} = 6$
$60 < a \leqslant 90$	6	9	$\frac{9}{6} = 1.5$

Example 6

Police conducted a survey into the speeds of vehicles on a motorway. The speeds were grouped in the ranges 0 to 30 mph, from 30 to 70 mph and from 70 to the maximum recorded speed of 120 mph.

In the table below the frequency densities have been calculated using the formula

$$\text{frequency density} = \frac{\text{frequency}}{\text{class width}}$$

Speed (*s*) in mph	Frequency density
$0 < s \leqslant 30$	8
$30 < s \leqslant 70$	42
$70 < s \leqslant 120$	5

(a) Work out the frequencies in each case.
(b) Work out the total number of vehicles in the survey.

(a) Rearranging the formula for frequency density gives

$$\text{frequency} = \text{class width} \times \text{frequency density}$$

so we have, in tabular form:

Speed (*s*) in mph	Class width	Frequency density	Frequency
$0 < s \leqslant 30$	30	8	$30 \times 8 = 240$
$30 < s \leqslant 70$	40	42	$40 \times 42 = 1680$
$70 < s \leqslant 120$	50	5	$50 \times 5 = 250$

(b) The total number of vehicles is the sum of the three frequencies, i.e.

$$240 + 1680 + 250 = 2170$$

Example 7

The incomplete histogram and table show some information about the salaries, in pounds, of the employees at Clifton Manor Hotel.

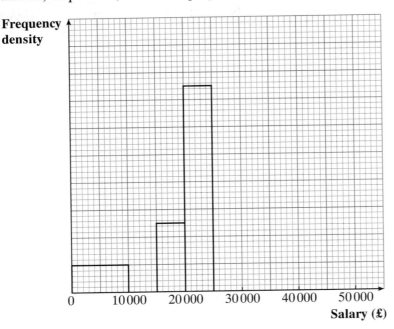

Salary (s) in pounds	Frequency
$0 \leqslant s < 10\,000$	4
$10\,000 \leqslant s < 15\,000$	6
$15\,000 \leqslant s < 20\,000$	
$20\,000 \leqslant s < 25\,000$	
$25\,000 \leqslant s < 30\,000$	8
$30\,000 \leqslant s < 50\,000$	4

(a) Use the histogram to complete the table.
(b) Use the table to complete the histogram.

(a) From the histogram, looking at the class interval
     $0 \leqslant s < 10\,000$ and comparing it with the table

     ☐☐ two squares = 4 people or ☐ = 2 people.

So from the histogram:

Class interval:	No. squares:	Frequency:
$15\,000 \leqslant s < 20\,000$	$2\frac{1}{2}$	$2 \times 2\frac{1}{2} = 5$
$20\,000 \leqslant s < 25\,000$	$7\frac{1}{2}$	$2 \times 7\frac{1}{2} = 15$

So the completed table is:

Salary (s) in pounds	Frequency
$0 \leqslant s < 10\,000$	4
$10\,000 \leqslant s < 15\,000$	6
$15\,000 \leqslant s < 20\,000$	5
$20\,000 \leqslant s < 25\,000$	15
$25\,000 \leqslant s < 30\,000$	8
$30\,000 \leqslant s < 50\,000$	4

(b) Using the table, the appropriate frequency densities (in terms of number of squares) are:

Class interval:	Frequency:	No. sqs (f.d.):
$10\,000 \leqslant s < 15\,000$	6	$6 \div 2 = 3$
$25\,000 \leqslant s < 30\,000$	8	$8 \div 2 = 4$
$30\,000 \leqslant s < 5000$	4	$4 \div 2 = 2$

So the completed histogram is

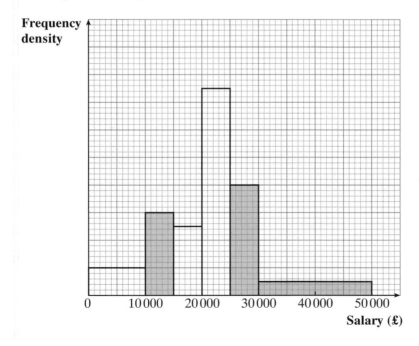

Exercise 10C   Links 27A

In these questions you may use either definition for frequency density unless told otherwise.

1   The age ranges of the members of a golf club are shown in the frequency table:

Age (a) years	Frequency
$0 < a \leqslant 20$	14
$20 < a \leqslant 30$	22
$30 < a \leqslant 40$	25
$40 < a \leqslant 45$	24
$45 < a \leqslant 50$	18
$50 < a \leqslant 60$	32
$60 < a \leqslant 70$	26
$70 < a \leqslant 85$	15

Work out and tabulate the frequency densities
(a) using class widths,
(b) using standard class intervals of 5 years,
(c) using standard class intervals of 10 years.

2   The ministry of transport conducted a survey of the speeds of vehicles on a main road. The results of the survey are given in the table opposite:
Work out and tabulate the frequency densities.

Speed (s) in mph	Frequency
$0 \leqslant s < 30$	12
$30 \leqslant s \leqslant 60$	59
$60 < s \leqslant 65$	15
$65 < s \leqslant 95$	15

3   There are 400 people living in the village of Shimpwell. Their ages are grouped and presented in the histogram. Work out and tabulate the frequency densities.

In the histogram,

$$\text{frequency density} = \frac{\text{frequency}}{\text{class width}}$$

Use the histogram to complete the grouped frequency table:

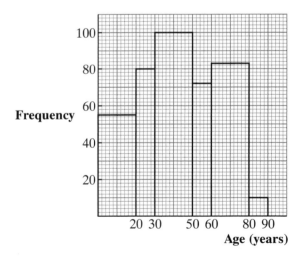

Age (a) in years	Frequency density
$0 \leqslant a < 20$	
$20 \leqslant a < 30$	
$30 \leqslant a < 50$	
$50 \leqslant a < 60$	
$60 \leqslant a < 80$	
$80 \leqslant a < 90$	

4 The weights of the Year 11 students at Goswell High School are grouped and presented below in the frequency density table.
The frequency density was worked out by dividing the frequency for each group by its class width.

Weight (w) kg	Frequency density
$30 < w \leqslant 40$	3.4
$40 < w \leqslant 50$	6.2
$50 < w \leqslant 55$	4.4
$55 < w \leqslant 60$	3.8
$60 < w \leqslant 85$	1.2

   (a) Work out the number of students in each age grouping.
   (b) Work out the total number of students in Year 11 at Goswell High School.

5 The waiting times for parents to see a teacher at parents evening were recorded.
The incomplete table and histogram show some of the results.

Waiting time in minutes (t)	Frequency
$0 \leqslant t < 10$	
$10 \leqslant t < 15$	20
$15 \leqslant t < 30$	
$30 \leqslant t < 35$	5
$35 \leqslant t$	0

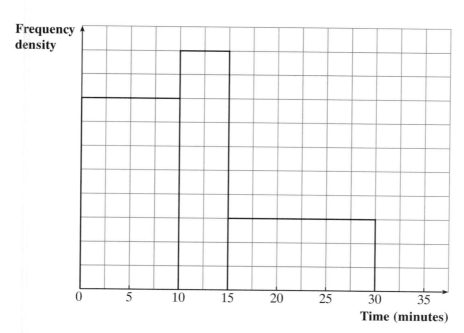

   (a) Use the histogram to complete the table.
   (b) Use the table to complete the histogram.

6   A sack contains some potatoes.

Information about the weights of the potatoes in the sack is presented in the incomplete table and incomplete histogram below.

Mass (*m*) grams	Frequency
$0 < m \leqslant 100$	
$100 < m \leqslant 150$	26
$150 < m \leqslant 200$	30
$200 < m \leqslant 250$	
$250 < m \leqslant 400$	12

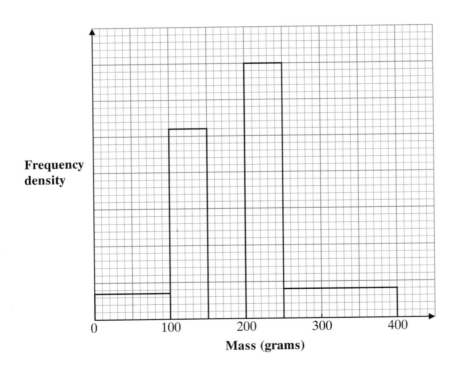

(a) Use the histogram to complete the table.

(b) Use the table to complete the histogram.

(c) Work out the number of potatoes in the sack.

(d) A potato is selected at random from the sack.
Work out the probability that this potato will weigh over 200 grams.

7 A sample of car owners were asked the distances, in miles, their car had travelled.
The unfinished histogram and table show some information about the responses.

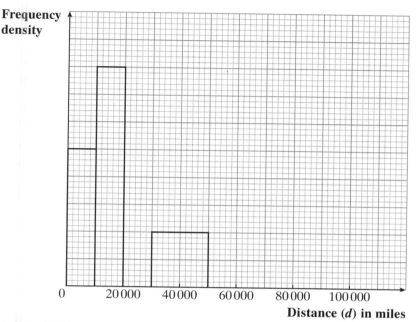

Distance (d) in miles	Frequency
$0 \leqslant d < 10\,000$	25
$10\,000 \leqslant d < 20\,000$	
$20\,000 \leqslant d < 30\,000$	20
$30\,000 \leqslant d < 50\,000$	
$50\,000 \leqslant d < 100\,000$	5

(a) Use the information in the histogram to complete the table.
(b) Use the information in the table to complete the histogram.

Summary of key points

- $P(\text{event}) = \dfrac{\text{the number of ways the event can occur}}{\text{the total number of possibilities}}$

- $\text{Relative frequency} = \dfrac{\text{number of times event occurs}}{\text{total number of trials}}$

- As the number of trials increases, the relative frequency approaches the probability of the event or outcome.

- Two events are mutually exclusive if the occurrence of one event means that the other cannot occur at the same time.

- When two events, A and B, are mutually exclusive

  $$P(A \text{ or } B) = P(A) + P(B)$$

- Two events are independent when the occurrence of one neither affects nor is affected by the occurrence of the other.

- When two events are independent

  $$P(A \text{ and } B) = P(A) \times P(B)$$

- $$\text{Frequency density} = \frac{\text{frequency}}{\text{class width}}$$

- An alternative for frequency density is

  $$\text{frequency density} = \frac{\text{frequency}}{\text{class width in standard class intervals}}$$

Examination style practice paper

Section 1   **Answer ALL SEVEN questions.**
            You must not use a calculator.

1   (a) Solve the inequality $4x + 9 \geqslant 3$.   (2)
     (b) Show the solution on a number line.   (1)

2 P
                                          •

     _____
     A B

     On a copy of the diagram, construct the perpendicular from
     the point P onto the line AB. You must show your method. (2)

3   (a) Write the number 0.007 in standard form.   (1)
     (b) Divide 4×10^9 by 5×10^4. Give your answer in standard
          form.   (2)

4   The length of each side of a regular octagon is measured
     correct to the nearest millimetre.
     The greatest possible perimeter of the octagon is 28.4 cm.

     Find the least possible perimeter of the octagon.   (2)

5   Sketch the graph of

     (a) $y = \dfrac{1}{x}$ for $x > 0$,

     (b) $y = 3^x$,
     (c) $y = \cos x$ for $0° \leqslant x \leqslant 360°$.   (3)

6   There are 3 red marbles and 2 blue marbles in a bag.
     Sophie takes a marble at random from the bag and replaces it.
     She then takes another marble at random from the bag.

     Find the probability that both the marbles she takes are the
     same colour.   (3)

7   Make a the subject of $4(a + 1) = 7 - ab$.

Section 2   **Answer ALL SIX questions.**
                  You may use a calculator.

1   When a radioactive element decays, its mass decreases by 16%
    every hour.
    (a) Calculate the percentage of the original mass which
         remains after 12 hours. Give your answer correct to 1
         decimal place.   (2)
    (b) Calculate the number of hours after which 29.5% of the
         original mass remains.   (2)

2   Mark spins a biased coin 40 times. It comes down Heads 31
    times.
    Calculate an estimate for the number of times he would expect
    the coin to come down Heads if he spins it 600 times.   (2)

3   (a) Expand and simplify $(x - 4)(x - 5)$.   (2)
    (b) Factorize $x^2 + 4x - 12$.   (2)

4   Solve the equation $x^2 - 5x - 3 = 0$
    Give your answers correct to 1 decimal place.   (3)

5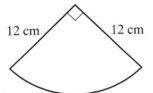

    12 cm   12 cm   Diagram NOT
                                accurately drawn.

    The diagram shows a sector of a circle, which is the net of the
    curved surface area of a cone.
    The radius of the sector is 12 cm and the angle at its centre is 90°.
    Find the radius of the base of the cone.   (4)

6   y is inversely proportional to x^2.
    $y = 4$ when $x = 5$.
    Express y in terms of x.   (2)

Answers

1 (a) $\frac{1}{3}$ (b) $\frac{1}{4}$ (c) $\frac{1}{a}$ (d) $\frac{1}{2a}$
   (e) $\frac{1}{y^3}$ (f) $\frac{4}{3}$ (g) $\frac{5}{2}$

2 (a) $\frac{1}{16}$ (b) $\frac{1}{64}$ (c) $\frac{1}{27}$ (d) $\frac{1}{16}$ (e) $6t$
   (f) 10 (g) 2 (h) 10 (i) $\frac{1}{5}$ (j) $\frac{1}{7}$
   (k) $\frac{1}{3}$ (l) $\frac{1}{4}$ (m) 1 (n) 1 (o) 16
   (p) 32 (q) 125 (r) $\frac{1}{100}$ (s) $\frac{1}{81}$ (t) $\frac{1}{32}$

5 (a) $h = 1.5\,s$
   (b) Length of shadow $= 6.4\,\text{m}$
   (c) Height of tree $= 18.9\,\text{m}$

6

x	4	6	10
y	15	10	6

7 5 drinks   **8** 18 cm

1 (a) x^5 (b) y^2 (c) a^2
   (d) t^{-1} (e) c^6 (f) $p^{\frac{3}{2}}$
   (g) z^5 (h) $r^{\frac{5}{6}}$ (i) s^{-5}
   (j) $3x$ (k) $\dfrac{5x^{-\frac{9}{2}}}{2}$

2 (a) $2^{-1} = \frac{1}{2}$ (b) $3^2 = 9$ (c) $8^{\frac{2}{3}} = 4$
   (d) $2^2 = 4$ (e) $6^{-2} = \frac{1}{36}$ (f) $4^0 = 1$
   (g) $8^2 = 64$ (h) $4^{\frac{1}{2}} = 2$ (i) $4^{-3} = \frac{1}{64}$ (j) $9^{-\frac{3}{2}} = \frac{1}{27}$

1 (a) 1.5×10^8 (b) 1.05×10^0 (c) 3.6×10^3
   (d) 3.84×10^6 (e) 3×10^{-7} (f) 4×10^3
   (g) 5×10^1 (h) 9×10^{-10}

2 (a) $210\,000\,000$ (b) 368 (c) $.00000304$
   (d) 15.5 (e) 0.00000008 (f) 0.0071

3 (a) $2800\,000$ (b) 2.7 (c) 3600
   (d) 0.0024 (e) $20\,000$ (f) 700
   (g) 2250 (h) 0.04

4 30 times   **5** 220 people per km^2

6 8.375×10^{-18}

1 (a) $\frac{1}{9}$ (b) $\frac{1}{3x}$ (c) $\frac{5}{4}$

2 (a) $\frac{1}{36}$ (b) 1 (c) $\frac{1}{8}$ (d) 7
   (e) 2 (f) 9 (g) $\frac{1}{9}$ (h) $\frac{1}{125}$

3 (a) y^{-1} (b) y^8 (c) $y^{\frac{11}{2}}$
   (d) $y^{-\frac{4}{3}}$ (e) $8y^{-2}$ (f) $2y^{-6}$

4 (a) $3^{-2} = \frac{1}{9}$ (b) $7^{-1} = \frac{1}{7}$ (c) $27^{\frac{5}{3}} = 243$
   (d) $25^{\frac{3}{2}} = 125$ (e) $10^{-3} = \frac{1}{1000}$ (f) $2^9 = 512$

5 (a) 1.15×10^7 (b) 1.24×10^2
   (c) 4×10^6 (d) 4.5×10^1

6 (a) 3600 (b) $0.000\,24$
   (c) $30\,000$ (d) 2.25×10^{-10}

7 7.344×10^{19} kg

1 $0.55\,\text{kg}$

2 (a) $V = \dfrac{10.9}{6.2}I$ (b) 7.56 volts (3 s.f.)

3 (a) $C = \dfrac{37.7}{6}r$ (b) $50.3\,\text{cm}$ (3 s.f.)

4 (a) $v = 0.003\,\text{m}$ (b) $1.275\,\text{kg}$ (3 s.f.)

1 (a) 128 grains   (b) 32 768 grains

2 (a) $16\,777\,216$ cells   (b) 3.74×10^{50} cells (3 s.f.)

3 $43\,680$

4 $1220\,\text{m}^3$ (3 s.f.)

5 (a) $58\,320$
   (b) $1\,574\,640$
   (c) 3.83×10^8 (3 s.f.)

6 4.7×10^7 (2 s.f.)

1 (a) $2\sqrt{7}$ (b) $3\sqrt{5}$ (c) $2\sqrt{2}$ (d) $3\sqrt{3}$ (e) $2\sqrt{15}$
   (f) $2\sqrt{3}$ (g) $\frac{2}{3}\sqrt{3}$ (h) $\frac{\sqrt{6}}{2}$ (i) $\frac{3}{5}\sqrt{3}$

2 Note that x can be two values – positive or negative
   (a) $x = 2\sqrt{5}$ or $-2\sqrt{5}$ (b) $x = 3\sqrt{2}$ or $-3\sqrt{2}$
   (c) $x = 2\sqrt{3}$ or $-2\sqrt{3}$

3 (a) Area $= 6\sqrt{2}$ (b) $AC = 3\sqrt{2}$

4 (a) Height $= \sqrt{6}$ (b) Area $= 6\sqrt{2}$

5 Area $= 36\pi\,\text{cm}^2$, circumference $= 12\pi\,\text{cm}$

6 (a) Radius $= 2\sqrt{3}\,\text{cm}$ (b) Circumference $= 4\sqrt{3}\pi\,\text{cm}$

1 (a) Smallest 11.5 cm
     Largest 12.5 cm
   (b) Smallest 10.015 m
     Largest 10.025 m
   (c) Smallest 5.5 cm
     Largest 6.5 cm
   (d) Smallest 9.005 m
     Largest 9.015 m
   (e) Smallest 7.995 m
     Largest 8.005 m

2 Between 22.5 km and 23.5 km

3 (a) Minimum 175
     Maximum 185
   (b) Minimum 530 050
     Maximum 530 150
   (c) Minimum 0.0015
     Maximum 0.0025
   (d) Minimum 0.003 15
     Maximum 0.003 25

4 Least upper bound 12.35 seconds
   Greatest lower bound 12.25 seconds

5 (a) 2.45 cm, 4.55 cm, 6.85 cm
   (b) 2.35 cm, 4.45 cm, 6.75 cm

Exercise 2E

1 Least upper bound = 14.3325 cm²
   Greatest lower bound = 13.5125 cm²
2 Least upper bound = 30.25π cm²
   Greatest lower bound = 20.25π cm²
3 Least upper bound = 9.56 cm (3 s.f.)
   Greatest lower bound = 9.33 cm (3 s.f.)
4 Least upper bound = 41.5 cm
   Greatest lower bound = 38.5 cm
5 Least upper bound = 8.66 m/s (3 s.f.)
   Greatest lower bound = 8.58 m/s (3 s.f.)
6 Least upper bound = 15 °C
   Greatest lower bound = 13 °C
7 Least upper bound = 0.47π m
   Greatest lower bound = 0.45π m
8 Least upper bound = 3.21 g/cm³ (3 s.f.)
   Greatest lower bound = 2.82 g/cm³ (3 s.f.)
9 Least upper bound = 1.35 (3 s.f.)
   Greatest lower bound = 1.27 (3 s.f.)
10 Least upper bound = 70
   Greatest lower bound = 21.4 (3 s.f.)

Exercise 2F

1 Absolute error = 14 g
   Percentage error = 3.5%
2 Absolute error = 0.12 m
   Percentage error = 4%
3 Absolute error = 0.8 litres
   Percentage error = 1.8% (1 d.p.)
4 Max. absolute error = 2.5 cm
   Percentage error = 1.4% (1 d.p.)
5 Max. percentage error = 1.56% (3 s.f.)
6 Max. absolute error = 4.125 cm²
   Max. percentage error = 13.75%
7 0.0151% (3 s.f.)
8 (a) Max. percentage error = 1.47% (3 s.f.)
   (b) Max. percentage error = 2.96% (3 s.f.)

Exercise 2G

1 (a) $V = 2.5I$ (b) 22.5 volts   (c) 3.4 amperes
2

a	25	15	9
b	36	60	100

3 (a) 18 414   (b) 1 491 534
4 (a) $2\sqrt{5}$ (b) $3\sqrt{7}$
   (c) $4\sqrt{3}$ (d) $\dfrac{\sqrt{3}}{2}$
5 Length = $3\sqrt{3}$ cm
6 Area = $(112 + 8\pi)$ cm²
7 (a) Length = 13.95 cm,   Width = 7.95 cm
   (b) Length = 14.05 cm,   Width = 8.05 cm
8 Least upper bound = 7.53 m/s (3 s.f.)
   Greatest lower bound = 7.40 m/s (3 s.f.)
9 Least upper bound = 5775
   Greatest lower bound = 1575
10 Absolute error = 2.3 litres
   Percentage error = 3.83% (3 s.f.)
11 Max. percentage error = 0.298% (3 s.f.)

Exercise 3A

1 (a)

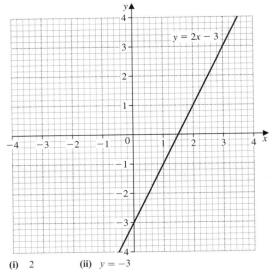

(i) 2   (ii) $y = -3$

(b)

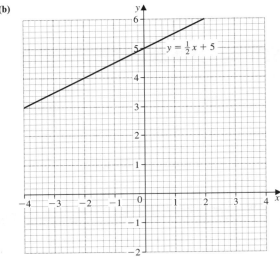

(i) $\frac{1}{2}$ (ii) $y = 5$

(c)

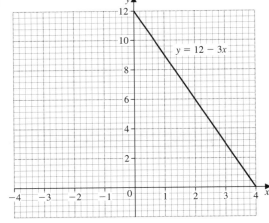

(i) -3 (ii) $y = 12$

(d)

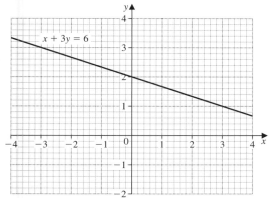

(i) $-\frac{1}{3}$ **(ii)** $y = 2$

(e)

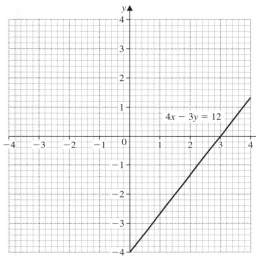

(i) $\frac{4}{3}$ **(ii)** $y = -4$

(f)

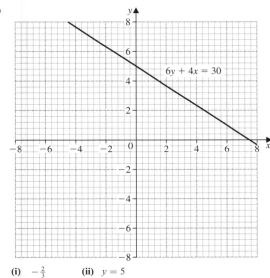

(i) $-\frac{2}{3}$ **(ii)** $y = 5$

2 (a) $y = 5 - 2x$
  (b) $y = -1 - 2x$
3 Gradient $= \frac{9}{4}$, intercept $= 6$

4 $y = 3x - 2$
5 Equation of AC: $y = \frac{1}{2}x + \frac{1}{2}$
   Equation of BD: $y = \frac{7}{2} - \frac{1}{2}x$
6 $m = 45$, $c = 30$

Exercise 3B

1 (a)

x	-3	-2	-1	0	1	2	3
y	17	7	1	-1	1	7	17

(b)

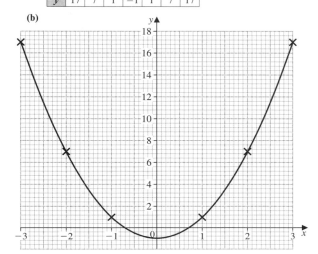

(c) (i) $x = 0.7$ and -0.7 (1 d.p.)
    (ii) $y = 11.5$
    (iii) $x = 2.6$ and -2.6

2 (a)

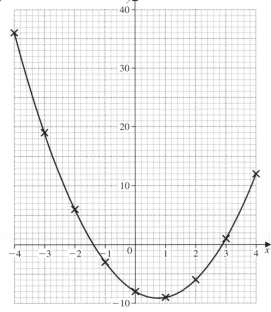

(b) $x = 2.9$ and -1.4 (1 d.p.)

3 (a)

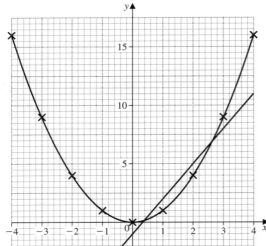

(b) $x = 0.4$ and 2.6 (1 d.p.)

4 (a)

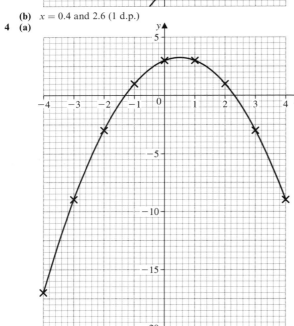

(b) $x = 2.3$ and -1.3 (1 d.p.)

5 $x = 1.15$ and -2.15

B

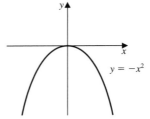

$y = -x^2$

C

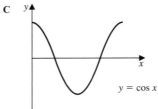

$y = \cos x$

D

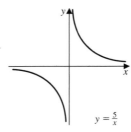

$y = \frac{5}{x}$

E

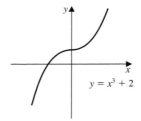

$y = x^3 + 2$

F

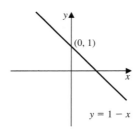

(0, 1)

$y = 1 - x$

Exercise 3C

1 A

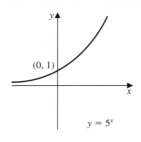

(0, 1)

$y = 5^x$

2

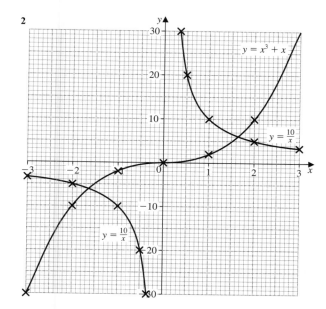

(b)

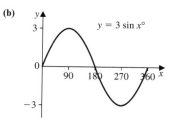

(c)

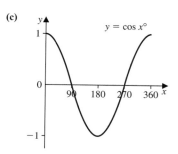

(d)

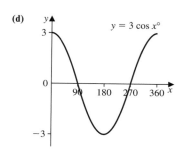

3

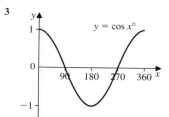

4

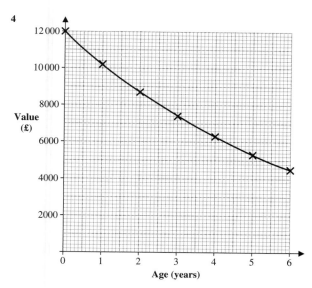

6

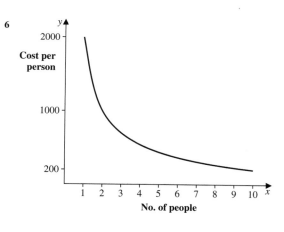

5 (a)

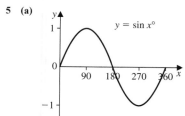

7

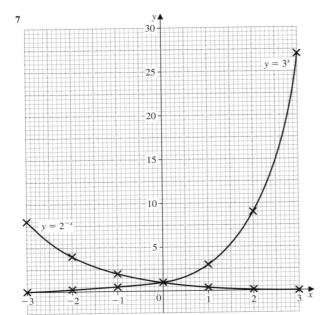

8

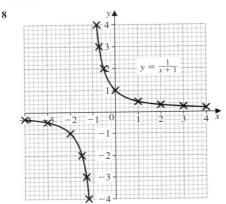

9   $y = 5 \sin x°$

10

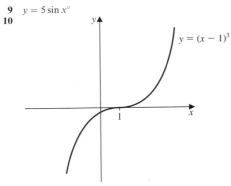

11   (a)

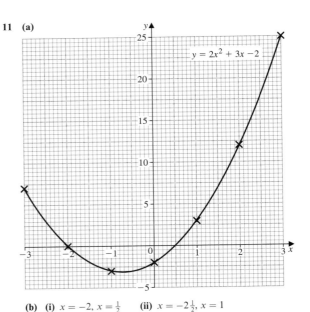

(b)   (i) $x = -2$, $x = \frac{1}{2}$ (ii) $x = -2\frac{1}{2}$, $x = 1$

(c)

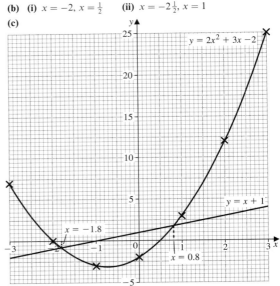

Approximate answers: $x = -1.8$, $x = 0.8$

(d) $2x^2 + 3x - 2 = x + 1$ can be simplified to $2x^2 + 2x - 3 = 0$

12   (a) $p = 12$, $q = 2$ (b)   (i) 192   (ii) 12

13   A is $(90°, 0)$; B is $(0°, 1)$

14   (a) $(90°, 1)$ (b) $(270°, -1)$

15   (a) $p = 2$, $q = 5$

(b)

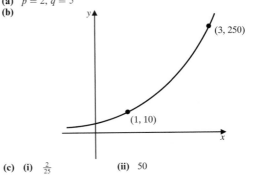

(c)   (i) $\frac{2}{25}$ (ii)   50

(d)   4

Exercise 4A

1   (a) $x^2 + 8x + 15$ (b) $x^2 + 7x + 12$
    (c) $x^2 + 10x + 16$ (d) $x^2 + 3x - 4$
    (e) $x^2 - 3x - 18$ (f) $x^2 + 2x - 24$
    (g) $x^2 - 12x + 27$ (h) $x^2 - 3x - 40$
    (i) $x^2 - 7x + 6$ (j) $x^2 - 64$
    (k) $x^2 - 8x + 12$ (l) $x^2 - 144$

2   (a) $ab + 5a + 4b + 20$ (b) $cd - 3c + 7d - 21$
    (c) $pq - 3p - 2q + 6$ (d) $xy + 7x - 5y - 35$
    (e) $at - 9a - 4t + 36$ (f) $bc - 8b + 5c - 40$

3   (a) $x^2 + 8x + 16$ (b) $x^2 - 2x + 1$
    (c) $x^2 + 14x + 49$ (d) $x^2 - 18x + 81$

4   (a) $3x^2 - 7x - 6$ (b) $6x^2 - 17x - 14$
    (c) $8x^2 - 22x + 15$ (d) $2xy + 4x - 7y - 14$
    (e) $10x^2 - 39x + 14$ (f) $10xy - 5x + 12y - 6$
    (g) $9x^2 - 49$ (h) $12x^2 + 51x + 45$
    (i) $25x^2 - 81$ (j) $4x^2 + 12x + 9$
    (k) $9x^2 - 30x + 25$ (l) $25x^2 + 10x + 1$
    (m) $49x^2 - 28x + 4$ (n) $10x^2 + 19xy + 7y^2$
    (o) $8x^2 - 4xy - 12y^2$ (p) $14x^2 - 41xy + 15y^2$
    (q) $25x^2 - 49y^2$ (r) $16x^2 - 8xy + y^2$
    (s) $18x^2 + 17xy - 15y^2$ (t) $9x^2 + 30xy + 25y^2$
    (u) $81x^2 - 4y^2$ (v) $64x^2 - 48xy + 9y^2$

5   (a) $x^2 + 2x - 6$ (b) $4x^2 - 2$
    (c) $2x^2 - 14x + 29$ (d) 11
    (e) $2x^2 + 10x + 37$ (f) $22x + 33$
    (g) $20x$ (h) $30e + 9$
    (i) $24x - 32$ (j) $9x^2 + 16x - 14$
    (k) $25x^2 - 26x + 7$ (l) x^2

Exercise 4B

1   (a) $x(3x + 5)$ (b) $3(3x^2 - 4)$
    (c) $x(x - 2)$ (d) $7(3x^2 + 1)$
    (e) $a(x^2 - 5)$ (f) $x(bx + 3)$
    (g) $7(x^2 - 4py)$ (h) $x(ax + b)$
    (i) $2(3x^2 - 4y)$ (j) $a(x^2 + y)$
    (k) $4(2ax^2 - by)$ (l) $x(1 - 5x)$

2   (a) $5x(x + 2)$ (b) $3x(3x - 2)$
    (c) $4x(3x - 1)$ (d) $5x(3x + 2)$
    (e) $ax(x - 4)$ (f) $3x(x + 2b)$
    (g) $cx(x - 2)$ (h) $ax(x + 1)$
    (i) $xy(x + y)$ (j) $4y(3xy + 2)$
    (k) $4x(2x + 3y)$ (l) $xy(2xy - 5)$
    (m) $3xy(2x + 5)$ (n) $2xy(5y - 4x)$
    (o) $3bx(2x + 1)$

3   (a) $(x + 1)(x + 3)$ (b) $(x - 3)(x + 1)$ (c) $(x - 2)(x - 1)$
    (d) $(x - 7)(x + 1)$ (e) $(x - 5)(x - 1)$ (f) $(x + 1)(x + 11)$
    (g) $(x + 1)^2$ (h) $(x - 11)(x + 1)$ (i) $(x - 4)^2$
    (j) $(x - 6)(x - 1)$ (k) $(x - 2)(x + 2)$ (l) $(x - 5)(x - 4)$
    (m) $(x - 5)(x + 4)$ (n) $(x + 3)^2$ (o) $(x - 8)(x + 8)$
    (p) $(x - 10)^2$ (q) $(x - 2)(x + 5)$ (r) $(x - 12)(x + 1)$
    (s) $(x + 3)(x + 5)$ (t) $(x - 7)(x - 2)$ (u) $(x - 5)(x + 6)$
    (v) $(x - 11)(x + 11)$
    (w) $(x + 5)^2$ (x) $(x - 7)(x + 4)$

4   (a) $(x - 1)(3x - 1)$ (b) $2(x - 5)(x + 5)$
    (c) $(x + 3)(2x - 1)$ (d) $3(x - 7)(x + 1)$
    (e) $(5x - 7)(x - 1)$ (f) $5(x - 2)(x + 2)$
    (g) $(3x + 2)^2$ (h) $7(x - 3)(x - 1)$
    (i) $(2x + 5)(4x - 1)$ (j) $(x + 6)(5x - 2)$
    (k) $4(x - 5)^2$ (l) $(3x - 4)(3x + 4)$
    (m) $(3x - 4)^2$ (n) $(2x + 1)(3x - 8)$
    (o) $3(x - 1)(2x + 5)$ (p) $(7x - 3)(7x + 3)$
    (q) $(3x - 2)(4x - 5)$ (r) $5(2x - 3)^2$
    (s) $(3x + 4)(5x - 3)$ (t) $7(2x - 1)(2x + 1)$
    (u) $(2x - 3)(7x + 6)$ (v) $(9x - 8)(9x + 8)$
    (w) $(2x - 1)(10x + 21)$ (x) $4(2x - 1)(3x - 2)$

Exercise 4C

1 $x + 2$ **2** $5(x - 6)^2$ **3** $\frac{1}{2}(x - 7)$ **4** $\dfrac{3}{x + 1}$

5 $\dfrac{3(x - 4)}{x + 2}$ **6** $\dfrac{2(x + 1)}{x - 5}$ **7** $\dfrac{x + 3}{x - 2}$ **8** $\dfrac{7x}{x + 4}$

9 $\dfrac{x + 1}{x - 1}$ **10** $\dfrac{x - 1}{4}$ **11** $\dfrac{2(x + 4)}{x + 1}$ **12** $\dfrac{x - 5}{x + 6}$

13 $5(x - 6)$ **14** $\dfrac{3(x - 1)}{4}$ **15** 3 **16** $\dfrac{x}{x + 7}$

17 $\dfrac{x + 4}{5x}$ **18** $\dfrac{2x(x + 5)}{5(x - 1)}$ **19** $\dfrac{x + 8}{x + 1}$ **20** $2(x - 5)$

Exercise 4D

1   (a) $P = \dfrac{V^2}{R}$ (b) $R = \dfrac{V^2}{P}$

2 $s = \frac{1}{2}gt^2$

3 $A = \dfrac{\pi d^2}{4}$

4 $a = r\omega^2$

5 $y = 2x + 5$

Exercise 4E

1 $I = \dfrac{P}{V}$ **2** $r = \dfrac{A}{\pi l}$ **3** $x = \dfrac{y + 3}{4}$

4 $n = \dfrac{t - 5}{3}$ **5** $y = P - 2x$ **6** $x = \dfrac{P - y}{2}$

7 $u = v + gt$ **8** $t = \dfrac{u - v}{g}$ **9** $b = \dfrac{2A}{h}$

10 $a = 2s - b - c$ **11** $M = VD$ **12** $V = \dfrac{M}{D}$

13 $v = \dfrac{I + mu}{m}$ **14** $u = \dfrac{mv - I}{m}$ **15** $h = \dfrac{2A}{a + b}$

16 $b = \dfrac{2A - ah}{h}$ **17** $x = 3(y + 2)$ **18** $x = \dfrac{y + 2}{2}$

19 $y = \dfrac{x - 6}{3}$ **20** $A = 2(17 - H)$ **21** $x = 5 - 2y$

22 $x = \dfrac{2y + 6}{3}$ **23** $y = \dfrac{3x - 6}{2}$ **24** $V = \dfrac{mv}{m + M}$

25 $c = \sqrt{\dfrac{E}{m}}$ **26** $a = \sqrt{c^2 - b^2}$ **27** $v = 10\sqrt{d}$

28 $R = \sqrt{\dfrac{A + \pi r^2}{\pi}}$ **29** $t = \dfrac{d - L}{La}$ **30** $a = \dfrac{kL - T}{k}$

31 $a = \sqrt{\dfrac{3I}{4M}}$ **32** $x = \sqrt{\dfrac{2aE}{L}}$ **33** $x = a(y - b)$

34 $f = \dfrac{uv}{u + v}$ **35** $u = \dfrac{vf}{v - f}$ **36** $x = \sqrt{2(y + 5)}$

37 $m = \dfrac{2E}{v^2 - u^2}$ **38** $a = \sqrt{\dfrac{3I - Mb^2}{M}}$ **39** $R = \dfrac{100(A - P)}{PT}$

40 $P = \dfrac{100A}{RT + 100}$ **41** $a = \dfrac{bx}{b - y}$ **42** $r = \sqrt{\dfrac{GMm}{F}}$

43 $D = \sqrt[3]{\dfrac{6V}{\pi}}$ **44** $L = \sqrt[3]{\dfrac{3EIx}{W}}$ **45** $r = \sqrt{\dfrac{12I - 4Ma^2}{3M}}$

46 $I = ma^2$ **47** $h = \dfrac{V^2}{2g}$ **48** $v = e = i^2 R$

49 $h = \dfrac{2d^2}{25}$ **50** $M = \dfrac{m}{R^2 - 3}$

Exercise 4F

1
(a) $x^2 + 11x + 18$ (b) $x^2 + 6x - 7$
(c) $x^2 - 10x + 16$ (d) $x^2 + 2x - 15$
(e) $x^2 - 9$ (f) $x^2 - 8x + 16$
(g) $x^2 + 16x + 64$ (h) $2x^2 - 9x - 35$
(i) $8x^2 - 14x + 3$ (j) $9x^2 - 1$
(k) $9x^2 - 6x + 1$ (l) $16x^2 + 56x + 49$
(m) $10x^2 - xy - 2y^2$ (n) $25x^2 - 40xy + 16y^2$
(o) $9x^2 - 16y^2$

2
(a) $x(4x + 7)$ (b) $9(3x^2 - 2)$
(c) $x(x + 1)$ (d) $8x(2x - 3)$
(e) $2ax(5x + 6)$ (f) $3xy(x - 3)$

3
(a) $(x + 1)(x + 7)$ (b) $(x + 2)(x - 1)$
(c) $(x - 4)(x - 3)$ (d) $(x - 8)(x + 8)$
(e) $(x - 9)(x + 2)$ (f) $(x - 9)^2$
(g) $3(x - 6)(x + 6)$ (h) $(x - 5)(3x - 4)$
(i) $(4x - 1)(4x + 1)$ (j) $(3x - 4)(4x + 1)$
(k) $(2x - 7)^2$ (l) $(4x + 1)(5x - 8)$

4
(a) $x - 5$ (b) $\dfrac{5}{x - 1}$ (c) $\dfrac{2(x - 7)}{3}$

(d) $\dfrac{4}{3(x + 2)^2}$ (e) $\dfrac{3(x + 2)}{2x - 1}$ (f) $\dfrac{8x}{x + 4}$

(g) $\dfrac{x - 3}{5(x + 3)}$ (h) $\dfrac{x + 2}{x - 1}$ (i) $\dfrac{x - 2}{x + 1}$

(j) $\dfrac{2}{x - 5}$ (k) $\dfrac{x + 4}{x}$ (l) $\dfrac{4(x + 1)}{3(x + 7)}$

(m) $\dfrac{(x - 10)(x - 2)}{(x + 1)(x + 10)}$

5
(a) $h = \dfrac{E}{mg}$ (b) $D = VT$ (c) $T = \dfrac{D}{V}$

(d) $I = \dfrac{V - e}{R}$ (e) $n = \dfrac{2S}{a + l}$ (f) $l = \dfrac{2S - na}{n}$

6
(a) $y = b(a - c)$ (b) $y = \dfrac{c - ab}{a}$ (c) $y = \sqrt{\dfrac{ac}{b}}$

(d) $y = \sqrt{\dfrac{a - c}{b}}$ (e) $y = \dfrac{c}{a - b}$ (f) $y = \dfrac{c}{a + b}$

(g) $y = \dfrac{ab - cd}{c - a}$ (h) $y = \sqrt{\dfrac{a - bc}{b}}$ (i) $y = \sqrt{\dfrac{c}{a - b}}$

(j) $y = \sqrt{\dfrac{b}{a + c}}$ (k) $y = \sqrt[3]{\dfrac{ac}{b}}$ (l) $y = \dfrac{a - bc}{c - 1}$

7 $E = \frac{1}{2}kx^2$

8 $y = 10t + 3$

9 $\dfrac{V = rS}{2}$

8 (a) — (b) — (c) — (d) — (e) — (f)

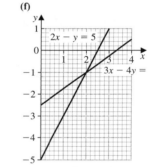
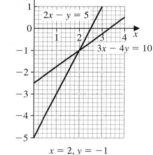

(a) $x = 5, y = 2$

(b) $x = 3, y = 5$

(c) $x = 3, y = 2$

(d) $x = 3, y = 5$

(e) $x = -2, y = 6$

(f) $x = 2, y = -1$

Exercise 5A

1
(a) $x = 0$ $x = 3$ $x = 7$
    $y = 7,$ $y = 4,$ $y = 0$
(b) $x = 3$ $x = 4$ $x = 5$
    $y = 0,$ $y = 1,$ $y = 2$
(c) $x = 0$ $x = 1$ $x = 2$
    $y = -3,$ $y = -1,$ $y = 1$
(d) $x = 0$ $x = 2$ $x = 8$
    $y = 4,$ $y = 3,$ $y = 0$
(e) $x = 0$ $x = 1$ $x = 3$
    $y = 3,$ $y = 2,$ $y = 0$
(f) $x = 0$ $x = 1$ $x = 2$
    $y = 5,$ $y = 3,$ $y = 1$

2 (a) Yes (b) No (c) No (d) Yes (e) Yes (f) No
3 (a) No (b) Yes (c) Yes (d) No (e) No (f) Yes
4 (a) Yes (b) Yes (c) Yes (d) No (e) Yes (f) Yes
5 (a) Yes (b) No (c) Yes (d) Yes (e) No (f) Yes
6 $x = -1, y = 3$ **7** $x = 3, y = 2$

Exercise 5B

1 $x = 2, y = 1$ **2** $x = 3, y = 1$
3 $x = 5, y = 0$ **4** $x = 3, y = -1$
5 $x = -1, y = -4$ **6** $x = 4, y = 2$
7 $x = 3\frac{1}{2}, y = 1$ **8** $x = -4, y = 3$
9 $x = -3, y = 1\frac{1}{2}$ **10** $x = 1\frac{1}{2}, y = -\frac{1}{5}$
11 $x = 2\frac{2}{3}, y = -1$ **12** $x = -2, y = -5$

Exercise 5C

1 $x = 4, y = 1$ **2** $x = 2, y = 5$ **3** $x = 4, y = 2$
4 $x = 1\frac{1}{2}, y = 2$ **5** $x = 2, y = -1$ **6** $x = -2, y = -3$
7 $x = 3, y = 4$ **8** $x = 2\frac{1}{2}, y = 3\frac{1}{2}$ **9** $x = 4, y = -2$
10 $x = 1\frac{1}{2}, y = -1$ **11** $x = 3\frac{1}{2}, y = 2\frac{1}{2}$ **12** $x = -\frac{1}{2}, y = -1\frac{1}{2}$

Exercise 5D

1 $x \leqslant 1$ **2** $x > -1$ **3** $-1 \leqslant x < 2$
4 $-3 < x < 3$ **5** $-3 < x \leqslant -1$ **6** $-3 \leqslant x \leqslant 0$
7

8

9

10

11

12

13

14

15

Exercise 5E

1 $x < 3$ **2** $x \geqslant \frac{1}{2}$ **3** $x > -5$
4 $x \leqslant -1$ **5** $x \leqslant -2$ **6** $x > 1$
7 $x > 2\frac{1}{2}$

8 $x < 1\frac{3}{4}$

9 $x \geqslant \frac{2}{3}$

10 $x < -\frac{1}{2}$

11 $x > 2\frac{1}{3}$

12 $x \leqslant 0$

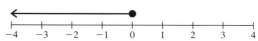

13 $x > -1\frac{1}{2}$

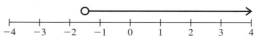

14 $x < 2\frac{2}{3}$

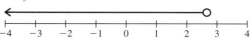

15 $x \geqslant -2\frac{1}{2}$

16 $x < 6\frac{1}{2}$ **17** $x \geqslant -1\frac{3}{4}$
18 $x > \frac{5}{7}$ **19** $x > -2$
20 $x \leqslant 1\frac{1}{2}$ **21** $x \leqslant -3\frac{2}{3}$
22 $x < \frac{3}{5}$ **23** $x \geqslant 2\frac{1}{5}$
24 $x > -\frac{2}{3}$

Exercise 5F

1 $-2, -1, 0, 1, 2$

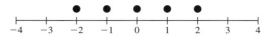

2 $-2, -1, 0, 1$

3 $1, 2, 3$

4 $-3, -2, -1$

5 $-1, 0$

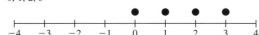

6 $0, 1, 2, 3$

7 $7, 8, 9$
8 $-6, -5$
9 $0, 1, 2$
10 $-5, -4, -3, -2, -1$
11 $-3, -2, -1, 0, 1$
12 $-1, 0, 1, 2, 3$
13 Greatest integer is 0
14 Least integer is -1
15 Greatest integer is 1

Exercise 5G

1

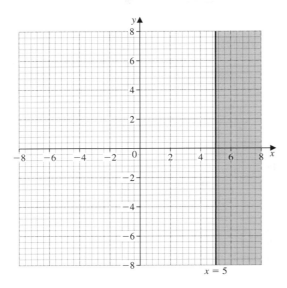

$x = 5$

2

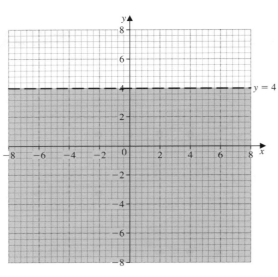

$y = 4$

3

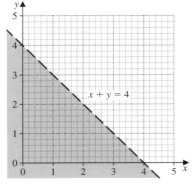

$x + y = 4$

4

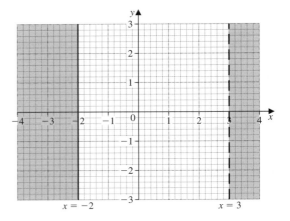

$x = -2$ $x = 3$

5

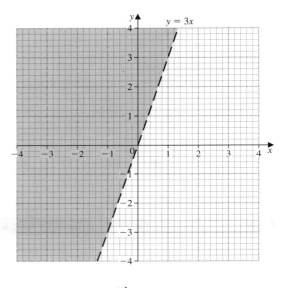

$y = 3x$

6

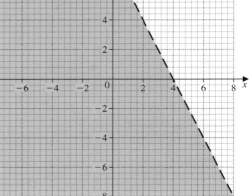

$2x + y = 8$

7

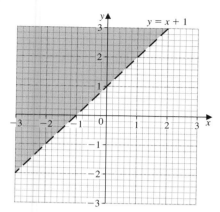

$y = x + 1$

8

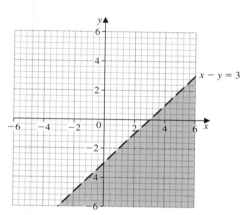

$x - y = 3$

9

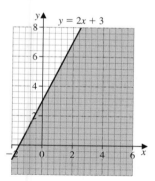

$y = 2x + 3$

10

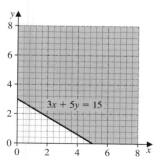

$3x + 5y = 15$

11

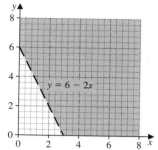

$y = 6 - 2x$

12

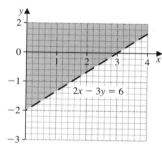

$2x - 3y = 6$

13 $y < 3$
14 $x + y \leqslant 2$
15 $y > x + 2$
16 $2x + 3y < 6$

17

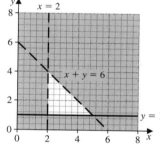

$x = 2$

$x + y = 6$

$y = 1$

18

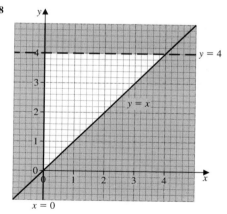

$y = 4$

$y = x$

$x = 0$

19

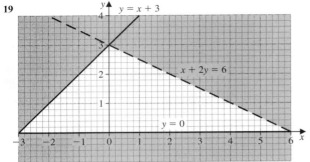

23

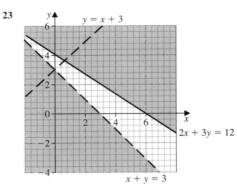

20

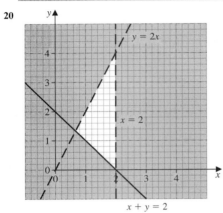

24

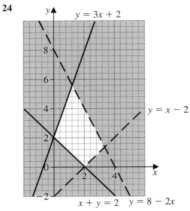

21

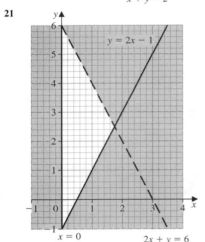

25

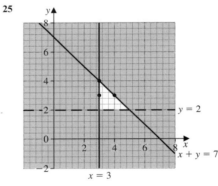

22

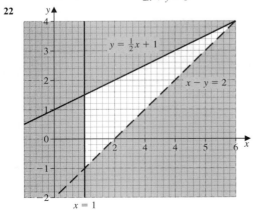

26

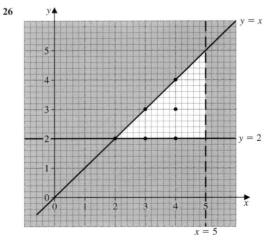

27

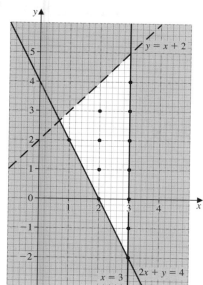

28

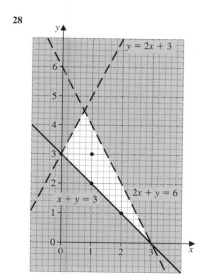

29

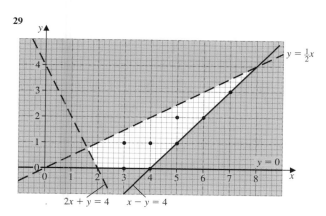

30

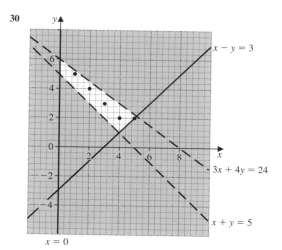

Exercise 5H

1 (a) $x = 4$ or $x = 5$ (b) $x = -3$ or $x = 8$
   (c) $x = -8$ or $x = -1$ (d) $x = 0$ or $x = 6$
   (e) $x = 7$ or $x = -2$ (f) $x = -9$ or $x = 9$
   (g) $x = 0$ or $x = -2$ (h) $x = -6$ or $x = 4$
   (i) $x = \frac{1}{2}$ or $x = \frac{2}{3}$ (j) $x = 2\frac{1}{2}$ or $x = -\frac{2}{5}$

2 (a) $x = 2$ or $x = 3$ (b) $x = 1$ or $x = -7$
   (c) $x = -8$ or $x = -2$ (d) $x = 0$ or $x = 5$
   (e) $x = -2$ or $x = 2$ (f) $x = 4$
   (g) $x = 0$ or $x = -9$ (h) $x = 5$ or $x = -4$
   (i) $x = -10$ or $x = 10$ (j) $x = -6$

3 (a) $x = 1$ or $x = 2$ (b) $x = 6$ or $x = -4$
   (c) $x = -1$ or $x = 1$ (d) $x = 0$ or $x = -6$
   (e) $x = -3$ or $x = -4$ (f) $x = 2$
   (g) $x = 0$ or $x = 7$ (h) $x = -5$
   (i) $x = -5$ or $x = 5$ (j) $x = 9$ or $x = -2$

4 (a) $x = 2$ or $x = -\frac{3}{5}$ (b) $x = 3$ or $x = -2\frac{1}{2}$
   (c) $x = \frac{1}{2}$ or $x = 1\frac{2}{3}$ (d) $x = 1\frac{1}{2}$ or $x = -1\frac{2}{5}$
   (e) $x = -2\frac{1}{2}$ or $x = 2\frac{1}{2}$ (f) $x = \frac{2}{3}$
   (g) $x = \frac{3}{4}$ or $x = \frac{2}{5}$ (h) $x = -3\frac{1}{2}$
   (i) $x = -\frac{2}{3}$ or $x = \frac{2}{3}$ (j) $x = -3\frac{1}{2}$ or $x = \frac{3}{4}$

5 (a) $x = 0$ or $x = \frac{1}{2}$ (b) $x = -4$ or $x = 4$
   (c) $x = -7$ or $x = 6$ (d) $x = 6$ or $x = -3$
   (e) $x = -2$ (f) $x = -5$ or $x = 3$
   (g) $x = 5$ (h) $x = \frac{1}{12}$ or $x = 1$
   (i) $x = \frac{2}{3}$ or $x = 2\frac{1}{2}$ (j) $x = -\frac{4}{5}$ or $x = \frac{4}{5}$

Exercise 5I

1 (a) $(x + 3)^2 - 9$ (b) $(x - 1)^2 - 1$
   (c) $\left(x + \frac{3}{2}\right)^2 - \frac{9}{4}$ (d) $(x + 4)^2 - 3$
   (e) $(x - 2)^2 + 3$ (f) $(x + 6)^2 - 6$
   (g) $(x - 5)^2 + 10$ (h) $(x + 10)^2 - 20$
   (i) $\left(x - \frac{5}{2}\right)^2 - \frac{9}{4}$

2 (a) $2(x + 1)^2 - 2$ (b) $3(x - 5)^2 - 75$
   (c) $5(x + 3)^2 - 45$ (d) $4(x - 2)^2 + 5$
   (e) $6(x + 3)^2 - 7$ (f) $7(x - 1)^2 + 3$
   (g) $3\left(x - \frac{1}{2}\right)^2 + \frac{1}{4}$ (h) $5\left(x + \frac{3}{2}\right)^2 - \frac{9}{4}$
   (i) $6\left(x - \frac{5}{2}\right)^2 - \frac{1}{2}$

Exercise 5J

1 (a) $x = 2 + \sqrt{5}$ or $x = 2 - \sqrt{5}$
   (b) $x = -4 + \sqrt{11}$ or $x = -4 - \sqrt{11}$
   (c) $x = 5 + \sqrt{17}$ or $x = 5 - \sqrt{17}$
   (d) $x = -3 + \sqrt{10}$ or $x = -3 - \sqrt{10}$
   (e) $x = -3 + \sqrt{\dfrac{13}{2}}$ or $x = -3 - \sqrt{\dfrac{13}{2}}$
   (f) $x = 2 + \sqrt{\dfrac{19}{3}}$ or $x = 2 - \sqrt{\dfrac{19}{3}}$
   (g) $x = \dfrac{5 + \sqrt{13}}{2}$ or $x = \dfrac{5 - \sqrt{13}}{2}$
   (h) $x = \dfrac{-9 + \sqrt{97}}{2}$ or $x = \dfrac{-9 - \sqrt{97}}{2}$

2 (a) $x = 1.24$ or $x = -3.24$
   (b) $x = 6.65$ or $x = 1.35$
   (c) $x = 5.45$ or $x = 0.55$
   (d) $x = 1.16$ or $x = -5.16$
   (e) $x = 0.22$ or $x = -2.22$
   (f) $x = 3.90$ or $x = 0.10$
   (g) $x = 2.62$ or $x = 0.38$
   (h) $x = 0.27$ or $x = -7.27$

Exercise 5K

1 (a) $x = \dfrac{3 + \sqrt{5}}{2}$ or $x = \dfrac{3 - \sqrt{5}}{2}$
   (b) $x = \dfrac{-5 + \sqrt{13}}{2}$ or $x = \dfrac{-5 - \sqrt{13}}{2}$
   (c) $x = 3 + \sqrt{11}$ or $x = 3 - \sqrt{11}$
   (d) $x = \dfrac{-7 + \sqrt{69}}{2}$ or $x = \dfrac{-7 - \sqrt{69}}{2}$
   (e) $x = \dfrac{-3 + \sqrt{15}}{2}$ or $x = \dfrac{-3 - \sqrt{15}}{2}$
   (f) $x = \dfrac{9 + \sqrt{57}}{6}$ or $x = \dfrac{9 - \sqrt{57}}{6}$
   (g) $x = \dfrac{-7 + \sqrt{17}}{8}$ or $x = \dfrac{-7 - \sqrt{17}}{8}$
   (h) $x = \dfrac{2 + \sqrt{19}}{5}$ or $x = \dfrac{2 - \sqrt{19}}{5}$
   (i) $x = \dfrac{-4 + \sqrt{10}}{3}$ or $x = \dfrac{-4 - \sqrt{10}}{3}$
   (j) $x = \dfrac{5 + \sqrt{73}}{8}$ or $x = \dfrac{5 - \sqrt{73}}{8}$

2 (a) $x = 0.45$ or $x = -4.45$
   (b) $x = 3.54$ or $x = -2.54$
   (c) $x = -0.68$ or $x = -7.32$
   (d) $x = 6.37$ or $x = 0.63$
   (e) $x = 2.69$ or $x = -0.19$
   (f) $x = -0.57$ or $x = -1.77$
   (g) $x = 1.81$ or $x = 0.69$
   (h) $x = 0.64$ or $x = -1.24$
   (i) $x = 1.64$ or $x = -2.14$
   (j) $x = 1.54$ or $x = 0.26$

3 (a) $x = 0.54$ or $x = -5.54$
   (b) $x = 0.54$ or $x = -5.54$
   (c) $x = 4.37$ or $x = -1.37$
   (d) $x = 7.16$ or $x = -0.84$
   (e) $x = 0.68$ or $x = -3.68$
   (f) $x = -0.63$ or $x = -2.37$
   (g) $x = 2.72$ or $x = 0.28$
   (h) $x = 0.40$ or $x = -1.24$
   (i) $x = 2.62$ or $x = 0.38$
   (j) $x = 2.22$ or $x = 0.45$

Exercise 5L

1 (a)

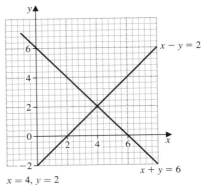

$x = 4$, $y = 2$

(b)

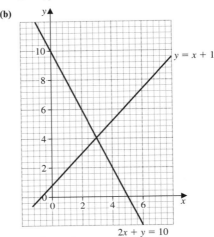

$x = 3$, $y = 4$

(c)

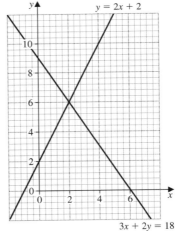

$x = 2$, $y = 6$

2 (a) $x = 4$, $y = 1$
   (b) $x = 3$, $y = -2$
   (c) $x = 1$, $y = 1\frac{1}{2}$

3 (a) $x = 3\frac{1}{2}$, $y = -1\frac{1}{2}$
   (b) $x = 4$, $y = 3$
   (c) $x = \frac{1}{2}$, $y = -3$

4 (a)

(b)

(c)

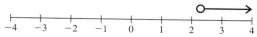

(b)

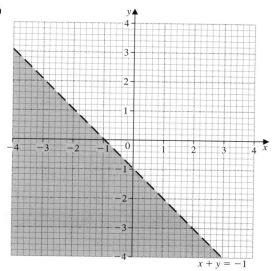

5 **(a)** $x \leqslant -1\frac{1}{2}$

(b) $x > 2\frac{1}{4}$

(c) $x \geqslant 0$

6 **(a)** $x < -\frac{4}{5}$
   (b) $x \geqslant 3\frac{1}{2}$
   (c) $x > \frac{2}{3}$

(c)

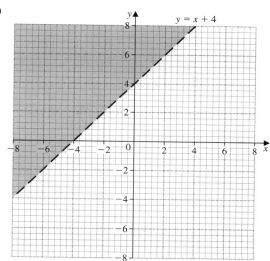

7 **(a)** $-3, -2, -1, 0$

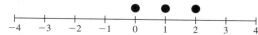

(b) $0, 1, 2$

(c) $-1, 0$

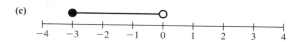

8 **(a)**

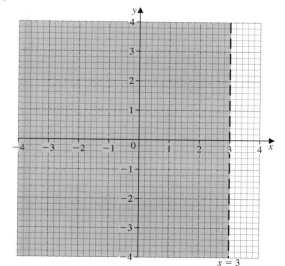

9 **(a) (b)**

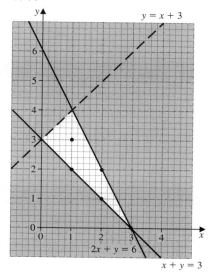

10 **(a)** $x = -7$ or $x = 5$
(b) $x = 0$ or $x = 10$
(c) $x = -9$ or $x = 9$
(d) $x = -4\frac{1}{2}$ or $x = 1\frac{2}{3}$
11 **(a)** $x = -5 + 4\sqrt{2}$ or $x = -5 - 4\sqrt{2}$
(b) $x = \dfrac{7 + \sqrt{33}}{2}$ or $x = \dfrac{7 - \sqrt{33}}{2}$
12 **(a)** $x = -1 + 2\sqrt{2}$ or $x = -1 - 2\sqrt{2}$
(b) $x = -2 + \frac{1}{2}\sqrt{6}$ or $x = -2 - \frac{1}{2}\sqrt{6}$
(c) $x = \dfrac{1 + \sqrt{73}}{6}$ or $x = \dfrac{1 - \sqrt{73}}{6}$
(d) $x = \dfrac{-9 + \sqrt{33}}{8}$ or $x = \dfrac{-9 - \sqrt{33}}{8}$

Exercise 6A

All answers to 3 s.f.
1 $4.28\,\text{cm}^2$ **2** $12.9\,\text{cm}^2$ **3** $15.9\,\text{cm}^2$
4 $10.2\,\text{m}^2$ **5** $18.0\,\text{m}^2$ **6** $156\,\text{m}^2$
7 $29.4\,\text{cm}^2$ **8** $75.0\,\text{cm}^2$ **9** $A = 30.6°$ or $149°$
10 $P = 148°$

Exercise 6B

1 **(a)** Arc $= \frac{4}{5}\pi\,\text{cm}$, perimeter $= 12 + \frac{4}{5}\pi\,\text{cm}$, area $= \frac{12}{5}\pi\,\text{cm}^2$
(b) Arc $= 4\pi\,\text{cm}$, perimeter $= 36 + 4\pi\,\text{cm}$, area $= 36\pi\,\text{cm}^2$
(c) Arc $= \frac{110}{3}\pi\,\text{cm}$, perimeter $= 120 + \frac{110}{3}\pi\,\text{cm}$, area $= 1100\pi\,\text{cm}^2$
(d) Arc $= 7\pi\,\text{cm}$, perimeter $= 9 + 7\pi\,\text{cm}$, area $= \frac{63}{4}\pi\,\text{cm}^2$
2 **(a)** Arc $= 6.0\,\text{cm}$, perimeter $= 36.0\,\text{cm}$, area $= 45.2\,\text{cm}^2$
(b) Arc $= 6.3\,\text{cm}$, perimeter $= 18.9\,\text{cm}$, area $= 19.7\,\text{cm}^2$
(c) Arc $= 11.6\,\text{cm}$, perimeter $= 23.4\,\text{cm}$, area $= 34.3\,\text{cm}^2$
(d) Arc $= 32.0\,\text{cm}$, perimeter $= 48.6\,\text{cm}$, area $= 132.9\,\text{cm}^2$
3 **(a)** $\theta = 43.0°$ (3 s.f.)   **(b)** $a = 24.6°$ (3 s.f.)
(c) $b = 115°$ (3 s.f.)   **(d)** $c = 306°$ (3 s.f.)

Exercise 6C

1 $520\,\text{m}^2$ **2** $344\,\text{m}^2$
3 $2969.1\,\text{m}^2$ (1 d.p.)   **4** $318.2\,\text{cm}^2$ (1 d.p.)
5 $138.2\,\text{cm}^2$ (1 d.p.)   **6** $339.3\,\text{cm}^2$ (1 d.p.)
7 $378\,\text{cm}^2$ **8** $516\,\text{cm}^2$
9 $339.3\,\text{mm}^2$ (1 d.p.)   **10** $596.9\,\text{cm}^2$ (1 d.p.)

Exercise 6D

1 **(a)** $75.4\,\text{m}^2$ (3 s.f.)   **(b)** $56.5\,\text{m}^3$ (3 s.f.)   **(c)** $283\,\text{m}^3$ (3 s.f.)
2 848 seconds (to nearest second)
3 $66\,000\,\text{cm}^3$
4 $6.41\,\text{cm}^3$ (3 s.f.)
5 $520\,\text{m}^3$
6 $2\,420\,000$ (3 s.f. but rounded down)

Exercise 6E

1 $47.1\,\text{cm}^3$ (3 s.f.)   **2** $11.2\,\text{cm}^3$ (3 s.f.)
3 $320\,\text{cm}^3$ **4** $3053.6\,\text{cm}^3$ (1 d.p.)
5 $45\,000\,\text{cm}^3$
6 **(a)** $111.3\,\text{m}^3$ (1 d.p.)
(b) 7.0 litres (1 d.p. but rounded up)

Exercise 6F

1 80.9 mph (3 s.f.)
2 58.2 km per hour (3 s.f.)
3 Total distance $= 28.25\,\text{km}$, overall average speed $= 40.4\,\text{kph}$ (3 s.f.)
4 $780.8\,\text{g}$
5 $16.3\,\text{g/cm}^3$ (3 s.f.)
6 $39.7\,\text{g}$ (3 s.f.)

Exercise 7A

Note that there may be more than one way to prove congruence.

1 Opposite sides of a rectangle are equal, so $AD = BC$
Clearly, $CD = CD$
And diagonals of a rectangle are equal, so $AC = BD$
So triangles ADC and BCD are congruent (SSS)
2 Opposite sides of a parallelogram are equal $\therefore PQ = RS$
Z-angles are equal $\left(\text{i.e.} \right)$ so $\angle QPX = \angle SRX$
and $\angle PQX = \angle RSX$.
Therefore SXR and QXP are congruent (ASA)
3 E is the mid-point of AC, so $AE = EC$
D is the mid-point of AB, so $AD = DB = FC$
Z-angles are equal, so $\angle DAE = \angle FCE$
So, DAE and FCE are congruent (SAS)
4 $ABCDE$ is a regular pentagon so $AB = BC$, $AE = CD$ and $\angle BAE = \angle BCD$
So, EAB and BCD are congruent (SAS)
5 Take the perpendicular from A to BC. Call the point where BC and the perpendicular cross M. AM is also perpendicular to XY.
Now, AMX and AMY are congruent (RHS) and AMB and AMC are congruent (RHS)
So, $MX = MY$, $MB = MC$ (so M is the midpoint of both BC and XY)
Therefore $BX = CY$
Since ABC and AXY are isosceles $AB = AC$ and $AX = AY$
So, BXA and CYA are congruent (SSS)
6 $WXYZ$ is a kite, so $WX = WZ$ and $XY = ZY$
Also, $WY = WY$
$\therefore WZY$ and WXY are congruent (SSS)
7 Bisect angle $\angle XBY$, let M be the point where bisector and XY cross. Then $\angle XBM = \angle YBM$, $BX = BY$ and $BM = BM$ so triangles XBM and YBM are congruent (SAS)
So $XM = MY$ and $\angle BMX = \angle BMY$, but since XY is a line we must have $\angle BMX = \angle BMY = 90°$
So, triangles AMX and AMY are congruent (RHS)
Therefore, $AX = AY$
Also, we have $BX = BY$ and $AB = AB$
So ABY and ABX are congruent (SSS)

8

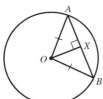

Call the centre of the circle O, and the end points of the chord A and B
Call the mid-point of the chord X.
$OA = OB$ (both radii)
$OX = OX$ (same)
$AX = XB$ (as X is mid-point of AB).
So triangles OAX and OXB are congruent (SSS)
Therefore $\angle AXO = \angle OXB$
Since AB is a straight line,
$\angle AXO = \angle OXB = 180° \div 2 = 90°$
Therefore OX is perpendicular to the chord

Exercise 7B

1

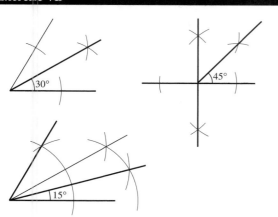

2 (a)

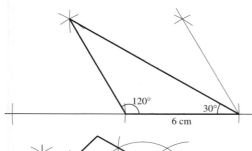

(b)

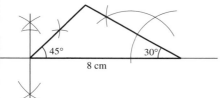

(c)

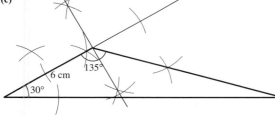

(d)

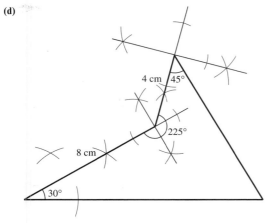

3 (a)

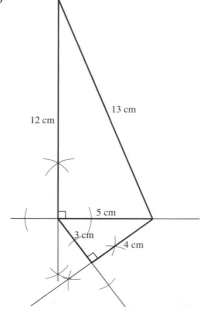

(b)

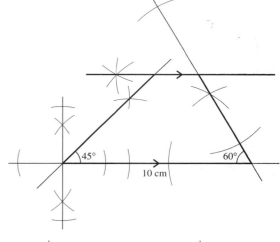

4

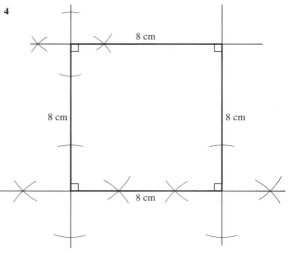

5 (a)

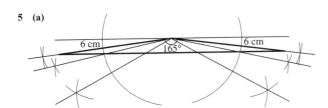

(b)

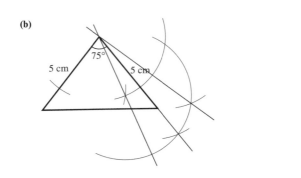

3

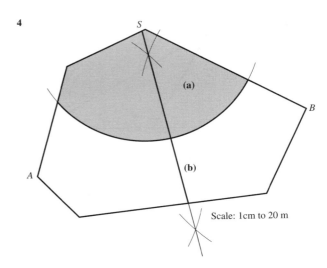

Exercise 7C

1

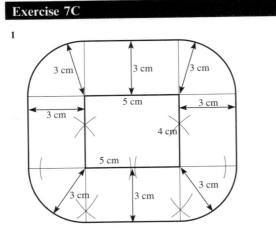

4

(a)

(b)

Scale: 1cm to 20 m

2

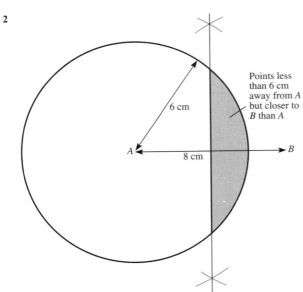

5

(b)

(a)

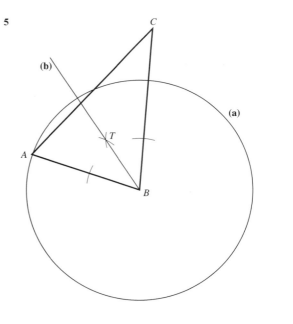

Exercise 8A

1 **(a)** **(i)** Under reflection, angles are unchanged.
    (ii) Under rotation, angles are unchanged.
    (iii) Under enlargement, angles are unchanged.
    (iv) Under translation, angles are unchanged.
 (b) **(i)** Under reflection, lengths are unchanged.
    (ii) Under rotation, lengths are unchanged.
    (iii) Under enlargement, lengths are multiplied by the scale factor.
    (iv) Under translation, lengths are unchanged.

Exercise 8B

1
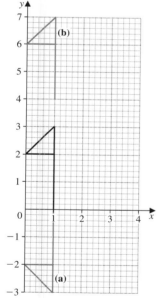
(c) Rotation about the origin through 180°

2
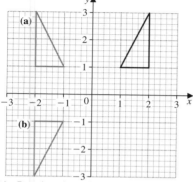
(c) Translation by $\begin{pmatrix} 0 \\ 4 \end{pmatrix}$

3
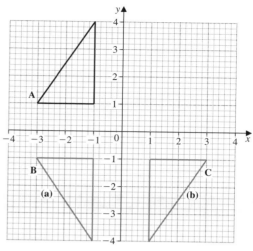
(c) Reflection in y-axis

4 **(a)**
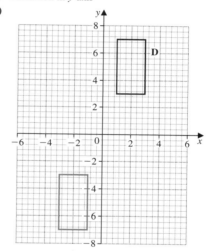
(b) Rotation about the origin through 180°

5
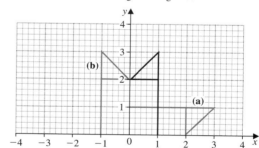
(c) Reflection in y-axis

6

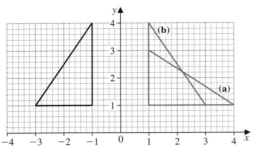

(c) Reflection in *y*-axis

Exercise 9A

1 (a) $\begin{pmatrix} -3 \\ 1 \end{pmatrix}$ (b) $\begin{pmatrix} 3 \\ -1 \end{pmatrix}$ (c) $\begin{pmatrix} -4 \\ -8 \end{pmatrix}$ (d) $\begin{pmatrix} -1 \\ -9 \end{pmatrix}$

2 (a) (i) $\begin{pmatrix} -2 \\ 2 \end{pmatrix}$ (ii) $\begin{pmatrix} 2 \\ -2 \end{pmatrix}$ (b) (2, 8)

3 (a) $\begin{pmatrix} 7 \\ 2 \end{pmatrix}$ (b)

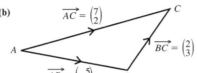

4 (a) (i) $\begin{pmatrix} 5 \\ -3 \end{pmatrix}$ (ii) $\begin{pmatrix} 1 \\ 7 \end{pmatrix}$ (iii) $\begin{pmatrix} 9 \\ 6 \end{pmatrix}$

(iv) $\begin{pmatrix} 4 \\ -10 \end{pmatrix}$ (v) $\begin{pmatrix} 5 \\ 16 \end{pmatrix}$

(b) (i)

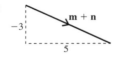

(ii)

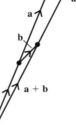

(iii)

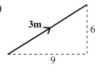

(iv)

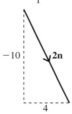

(v)

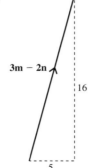

5 (a) $\begin{pmatrix} -3 \\ 5 \end{pmatrix}$ (b) $\begin{pmatrix} 3 \\ -5 \end{pmatrix}$ (c) $x = \begin{pmatrix} 1 \\ -\frac{1}{2} \end{pmatrix}$

6 (a)

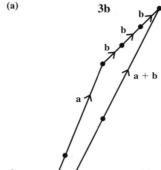

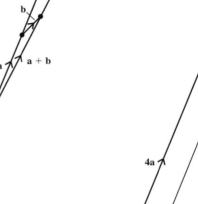

Exercise 9B

1 $x = \begin{pmatrix} 4 \\ 3 \end{pmatrix}$ 2 $y = \begin{pmatrix} -1 \\ -4 \end{pmatrix}$

3 $z = \begin{pmatrix} -6 \\ 5 \end{pmatrix}$

4 (a) $5\mathbf{a} - 3\mathbf{b}$ is parallel to x-axis
 (b) $3\mathbf{a} - 2\mathbf{b}$ is parallel to y-axis
5 $p = -2$
6 $p = 2\frac{1}{5}, q = 1\frac{1}{5}$
7 $\frac{9}{7}\mathbf{a} + \frac{4}{7}\mathbf{b} = \begin{pmatrix} 2 \\ 5 \end{pmatrix}$

Exercise 9C

1 Let M be the mid-point of AB. $\overrightarrow{OM} = \begin{pmatrix} 5 \\ 5 \end{pmatrix}$
2 $\overrightarrow{OC} = \mathbf{c} = \frac{4}{5}\mathbf{a} + \frac{1}{5}\mathbf{b}$
3 Coordinates of C are $(5, -1)$
4 (a) (i) $\left(2\frac{1}{2}, 3\frac{1}{2}\right)$ (ii) $\left(1, \frac{1}{2}\right)$
  (iii) $\left(\frac{1}{2}, 2\right)$
 (b) Coordinates of G are $(1, 8)$
5 $\overrightarrow{OD} = \begin{pmatrix} -5 \\ -1 \end{pmatrix}$

Let M be the mid-point of BD, $\overrightarrow{OM} = \begin{pmatrix} -4\frac{1}{2} \\ 3\frac{1}{2} \end{pmatrix}$

Exercise 9D

1 (a) $\begin{pmatrix} -3 \\ 1 \end{pmatrix}$ (b) $\begin{pmatrix} 4 \\ -10 \end{pmatrix}$ (c) $\begin{pmatrix} -4 \\ 10 \end{pmatrix}$ (d) $\begin{pmatrix} 7 \\ -11 \end{pmatrix}$

2 (a) $\begin{pmatrix} 3 \\ 6 \end{pmatrix}$ (b) $\begin{pmatrix} -7 \\ 0 \end{pmatrix}$ (c) $\begin{pmatrix} -6 \\ 9 \end{pmatrix}$ (d) $\begin{pmatrix} 16 \\ -3 \end{pmatrix}$

3 (a) $\begin{pmatrix} 1 \\ -3 \end{pmatrix}$ (b) $\begin{pmatrix} 13 \\ 11 \end{pmatrix}$ (c) $x = \begin{pmatrix} \frac{1}{2} \\ 1 \end{pmatrix}$

4 $x = \begin{pmatrix} -4 \\ 5 \end{pmatrix}$

5 $3\mathbf{a} - 5\mathbf{b}$ is parallel to the y-axis
6 $p = 2, q = 3$
7 $\overrightarrow{OC} = \mathbf{c} = \frac{2}{3}\mathbf{a} + \frac{1}{3}\mathbf{b}$
8 M and N are the mid-points of OA and
 OB, so $\overrightarrow{OM} = \frac{1}{2}\overrightarrow{OA}$ and $\overrightarrow{ON} = \frac{1}{2}\overrightarrow{OB}$
 $\therefore \overrightarrow{MN} = \overrightarrow{ON} - \overrightarrow{OM} = \frac{1}{2}\overrightarrow{OA} - \frac{1}{2}\overrightarrow{OB}$
   $= \frac{1}{2}\left(\overrightarrow{OA} - \overrightarrow{OB}\right) = \frac{1}{2}\overrightarrow{AB}$ or $\overrightarrow{AB} = 2\overrightarrow{MN}$
 This shows AB is parallel to MN, and twice the length.
9 (a) $\overrightarrow{AM} = \mathbf{b} + \frac{1}{2}\mathbf{c}, \overrightarrow{DC} = \frac{2}{3}\mathbf{b} + \frac{1}{3}\mathbf{c}$
 (b) $\overrightarrow{AM} = \frac{3}{2}\overrightarrow{DC}$ so $AM:DC = 3:2$ and clearly AM and DC are parallel

Exercise 10A

1 (a) $\frac{1}{5}$ (b) $\frac{3}{5}$ (c) $\frac{13}{20}$ (d) $\frac{3}{10}$
2 Take a sample of trains by doing a survey, and count how many trains are late. The number of trains that are late divided by the total number of trains in the survey is an estimate for the probability of a train being late. The larger the sample, the more accurate the estimate.
3 (a) (i) Estimate for the probability of match finishing with exactly 4 goals scored is 0.11, since from the results in the survey the number of matches ending with 4 goals scored was 22 out of 200.

 (ii) Estimate for the probability of match finishing with 4 or more goals scored is 0.19, since from the results in the survey the number of matches ending with 4 or more goals scored was 38 out of 200.
 (b) Estimate for the most likely number of games to be played in which exactly 3 goals will be scored is 2496
4 Estimate for the likely number of times spinner will land on **B** is 108

Exercise 10B

1 (a) 0.63
 (b) 0.07
 (c) 0.97
2 (a) 0.15
 (b) (i) 0.0324 (ii) 0.1704 (3 s.f.) (iii) 0.0925
3 (a) 0.48
 (b) 0.92
4 (a) 0.225
 (b) 0.475
 (c) 0.525
5 (a) $\frac{1}{32}$ (b) $\frac{31}{32}$
6 (a)

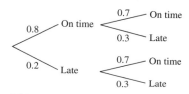

 (b) 0.06 (c) 0.44
7 (a)

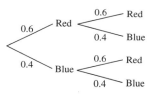

 (b) 0.36 (c) 0.48
8 0.92

Exercise 10C

1 (a), (b), (c)

Age (a) years	Frequency density for (a), (b) and (c)		
$0 < a \leqslant 20$	0.7	3.5	7
$20 < a \leqslant 30$	2.2	11	22
$30 < a \leqslant 40$	2.5	12.5	25
$40 < a \leqslant 45$	4.8	24	48
$45 < a \leqslant 50$	3.6	18	36
$50 < a \leqslant 60$	3.2	16	32
$60 < a \leqslant 70$	2.6	13	26
$70 < a \leqslant 85$	1	5	10

Class widths   Standard class interval of 5 years   Standard class interval of 10 years

2

Speed (*s*) in mph	Frequency density
$0 \leqslant s < 30$	0.4
$30 \leqslant s \leqslant 60$	1.97
$60 < s \leqslant 65$	3
$65 < s \leqslant 95$	0.5

(Class widths used to calculate the frequency density)

3

Age (*a*) years	Frequency density
$0 < a \leqslant 20$	2.75
$20 < a \leqslant 30$	8
$30 < a \leqslant 50$	5
$50 < a \leqslant 60$	7.2
$60 < a \leqslant 80$	4.15
$80 < a \leqslant 90$	1

(Class widths used to calculate the frequency density)

4 (a)

Weight (*w*) kg	Frequency
$30 < w \leqslant 40$	34
$40 < w \leqslant 50$	62
$50 < w \leqslant 55$	22
$55 < w \leqslant 60$	19
$60 < w \leqslant 85$	30

(b) Total number of students = 167

5 (a)

Weight time in minutes (*t*)	Frequency
$0 \leqslant t < 10$	32
$10 \leqslant t < 15$	20
$15 \leqslant t < 30$	18
$30 \leqslant t < 35$	5
$35 \leqslant t$	0

(b)

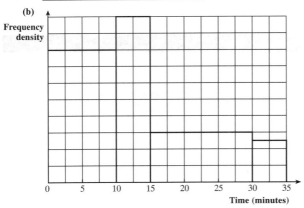

6 (a)

Mass (*m*) grams	Frequency
$0 < m \leqslant 100$	7
$100 < m \leqslant 150$	26
$150 < m \leqslant 200$	30
$200 < m \leqslant 250$	35
$250 < m \leqslant 400$	12

(b)

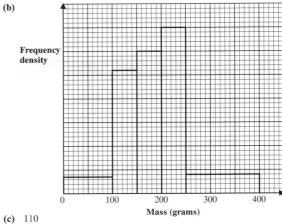

(c) 110
(d) 0.43 (2 d.p.)

7 (a)

Distance (*d*) in miles	Frequency
$0 \leqslant d < 10\,000$	25
$10\,000 \leqslant d < 20\,000$	40
$20\,000 \leqslant d < 30\,000$	20
$30\,000 \leqslant d < 50\,000$	20
$50\,000 \leqslant d < 100\,000$	5

(b)

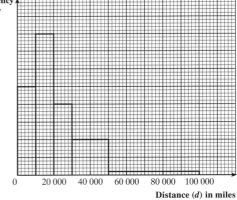

Examination style practice paper

Section 1
1 (a) $x \geqslant -1\frac{1}{2}$
(b)

2

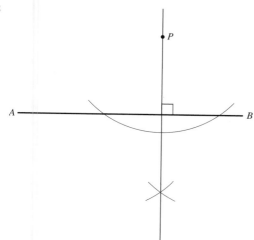

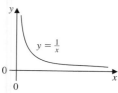

Method: Use compasses to draw an arc with centre at P to intersect the line AB in two places. Now the perpendicular bisector of the line between these points will pass through P, and so be the line we require. So contine as when finding the perpendicular bisector (i.e. find the intersection of arcs with centres at these points, then join this to P with a straight line)

3 (a) 7×10^{-3}
   (b) 8×10^4
4 27.6 cm
5 (a)

(b)

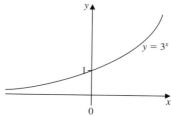

(c)

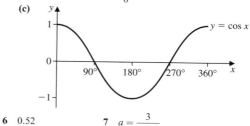

6 0.52

7 $a = \dfrac{3}{4 + b}$

Section 2

1 (a) 12.3%
   (b) 7 hours
2 Estimate is 465 times
3 (a) $x^2 - 9x + 20$
   (b) $(x + 6)(x - 2)$
4 $x = 5.5$ or $x = -0.5$
5 Radius $= 3$ cm
6 $y = \dfrac{100}{x^2}$